French Cricket

by
George East

French Cricket

Published by
La Puce Publications (UK)
87 Laburnum Grove
North End
Portsmouth PO2 0HG

Telephone: 023 92 678148
Facsimile: 023 92 665070
e-mail: info@la-puce.co.uk
website: www.la-puce.co.uk

© George East 2002

This paperback edition 2002

ISBN 0 9523635 6 9

The author asserts the moral right to
be identified as the author of this work

Designed and typeset by Nigel at Christianson Hoper Norman
Reprographics by SP Digital
Printed in Great Britain by Borcombe Printers PLC, Hampshire

For my brother.
See you later, John.

Books in the Mill of the Flea series:

Home & Dry in France
(A Year in Purgatory)

René & Me
(A Year with the Normandy Fox)

French Letters

French Flea Bites

French Cricket

———————————————

Also by the same author:

A Year Behind Bars

LA PUCE PUBLICATIONS (UK)
87 Laburnum Grove, Portsmouth PO2 OHG
Telephone: 023 92 678148 Facsimile: 023 92 665070
e-mail: info@la-puce.co.uk
Website: www.la-puce.co.uk

Author's Disclaimer

The most common question I am asked by people kind enough to read my books is whether the characters and events are real. Actually, that's not true.

What most readers ask is if I really expect them to believe that such characters exist, and such bizarre things happen around my wife and I.

My answer is usually yes... and no.

The locations featured in the Mill of the Flea series are mostly real, and so are most of the situations and some of the characters. The rest are either composites of real places, events and people, or, just now and then, complete figments of my imagination.

Sometimes I wish I could tell the plain, unvarnished truth, as some of the things that happen to us are beyond even my wildest imaginings. But, over the years, I have found this way of doing things the best way to avoid legal action, hurt feelings, and, particularly, the occasional punch in the nose.

13th April:

A soft rain falls. I am sitting by the grotto, watching a goose dance to a Beethoven sonata. At the hen house formerly known as my tool shed, the escape committee will be hatching the evening's breakout plan. At the big pond, my wife is giving swimming lessons to a duck that is afraid of water.

We returned to the Mill of the Flea only a week ago, but life is clearly getting back to normal.

In China and Japan, the goose is said to be a gift from heaven and bringer of glad tidings. I hope this is true, as we are sorely in need of good news. It has been a painful two years away from our Normandy home, and La Puce is looking shabby, neglected and somehow reproachful.

The once-white walls of the cottage and farmhouse are the colour of the Widow of Négreville's teeth, and the rain of two hard winters has stripped every inch of creosote from the sheds, gates and fencing. The wooden bridge across the mill pond has become a place of danger, and the twee post box at the top of the track has collapsed in apparent despair of its surroundings.

But now we are back we can soon repair the damage, and there is much else to do. I have a new book to write about our small adventures in Lower Normandy, and more schemes to dream up to try and keep us financially afloat. My wife will have her hands full with restoring the land, rebuilding her menagerie and repairing her broken cement mixer. Most importantly, we will need to get back into the rhythm and pace of life in the Cotentin. Here, we are no more than a hundred miles from the southern coast of England, but it often seems light years away.

Across the Channel, sadness and loss have been frequent visitors. Now, as my wife says, it is time to look to the future and remake our lives at the Mill of the Flea.

An author is a man who lives off the fat of the land. The trouble is that it is always someone else's land.

Geoffrey Woolard (farmer and philosopher).

ONE

Last night I dreamed I went to Mandalay again. As I have never visited that place even once, it must have been the goat cheese rarebit we had for supper.

It is a breathless day, with not a whisper of breeze to relieve the relentless heat. Our local immortal Old Pierrot is already predicting the hottest summer since he arranged a series of celebratory barbecues for William the Conqueror, and 1067, if he remembers rightly, was a real scorcher.

Far above the clay tiles baking on the mill cottage roof, a buzzard wheels lazily through the shimmering haze, but even he seems too lethargic to swoop down in search of his midday meal. I have taken refuge in the tree-shrouded water basin we call our grotto, and am sitting cross-legged and palely naked beneath the cascade. The water is deliciously cold, even on such a roasting day. My wife says I will frighten the fish, but I have pointed out that my presence will also scare the poachers away, so she is content to let me while away the day planning the new book and thinking about thinking about finally restoring the Mill of the Flea.

What remains of our tiny 18th-century water mill was built to service the estate of the *Château du Lude*, for which the lively stream running through our land is named. Or perhaps it was the other way round.

For certain, two hundred and more years ago, and perhaps on a golden day like this, the miller would be lowering a great stone slab to divert the Lude into the water meadow and create a lake to power the wheel and bring the Mill of the Flea to life. A procession of creaking carts would be trundling down the track, laden with fat sacks of grain from any one of a thousand tree-lined fields on the Lude estate. By the stone bridge, a horse would have shed a shoe, and the cursing driver could not possibly imagine that a poor English writer digging for the miller's gold would find it centuries later. Over at the stone chute, local women would quite literally be washing their dirty linen in public, and for once the talk would not be of local affairs, but of terror and revolution and death in Paris, and the doomed dreams of liberty, fraternity and equality for all the citizens of France.

Now, the massive oaken wheel, the grinding stones and even the roof and walls of the working end of the Mill of the Flea have gone with the people and their hopes for a better life, and only the ghosts of the past remain. All that is left of the once-thriving mill is what we and our slim resources could make of it.

Downstairs in the cottage, a porch leads to one large and always cool and dark room, which has an old butler's sink, a cooker and some rickety shelving fitted in one corner. At the far end of the room, a pair of mismatching chairs and an old sofa confront the wood-burning stove that my friend the Fox of Cotentin found for us in a carelessly unlocked barn. By the door, a roughly made staircase leads to the attic. Beneath the rafters is a small bedroom, with a bathtub and toilet sitting immodestly in one corner. On the cramped landing is a sofabed for small guests, and behind the bed is a cupboard which is the home of our non-paying guests, the mouse family. Even though they contribute nothing to the household, they have considerably more room than us and like to eat the electricity cables, but my wife will not allow me to lace their regular cheese treats with poison.

Outside, the roughly triangular ten acres of woodland, fields, streams, ponds and scrub of La Puce is bordered on one side with what counts as a main road in rural Normandy, and thousands of hectares of mostly unfarmed land on the other. There is another cottage alongside the noisy road which we try to rent to deaf French tenants, but the home of our hearts has always been the remnants of *le Moulin de la Puce*.

What is left of the Mill of the Flea and its environs is not most people's idea of a picturesque and ancient water mill. There is no wide river and gently turning wheel, interesting machinery or characterful stone-flagged floor burnished with time. Though the walls and roof keep out most of the winter rain, it can be a dank and gloomy place on the mildest of days. But it is our home, and we like it. Though people today might not think of our accommodations as remotely comfortable, those who lived and worked at the mill all those years ago would have thought of them as almost impossibly luxurious. Our life of comparative ease here would be more than they could dream of, even had the Revolution and all that followed lived up to its promise. In our self-concerning modern world, that is surely a thought worth thinking as I sit in the bubbling cascade on this endlessly glorious day.

The sun shines on, and I am on my way to market with instructions to buy a mate for Ermintrude, our balletic goose.

With some women it is shoes or clothing. With my wife it is animals. She says she finds them more intelligent, logical and sensitive than most people, and infinitely better company. The feeling is obviously reciprocal, as every wild or abandoned domestic animal in the area knows where to come for protection, unequivocal love and at least three square meals a day. My wife is sure that our latest refugee is a female (as no male of any species could move so gracefully), so I am to find a suitable gander. There should be a plentiful supply of male geese at the market, but my specific instructions are that Ermintrude's mate must also be of distinguished bearing, engaging disposition and, preferably, demonstrate a liking for classical music.

We found the latest addition to Donella's menagerie when we arrived at La Puce, and I can think of no better homecoming present for my wife. A lively piece by Bach was playing on the car radio, and as we came to a halt at the bottom of the mill track, a large grey goose waddled towards us, honking as if in welcome. We sat and watched as it went through what looked like a series of delicate leg-stretching exercises, and then began to twirl around as if in time to the music. Even I was moved at the sight of such a normally ungainly bird moving so gracefully in the moonlight, and my wife cried at such an unexpected and delightful welcome home. She is sure that Ermintrude is a symbol of hope for the future, and is indeed a gift from the benevolent gods of nature. I prefer to think that she is an escapee from the *foie gras* farm downstream.

Knowing how happy her arrival has made my wife and how they fatten their geese at the farm, I am for once content to have yet another mouth to feed. Ironically, our new refugee will now probably be given more maize each day than her former companions, but will not need to have a metal funnel forced savagely down her throat to take it.

It is market day, so the road to Bricquebec is busier than usual. I have been enjoying the weekly tradition of exchanging cheerful and ever-more inventive insults with overtaking motorists who think I should travel at seventy miles an hour round blind bends, or get out of their way by driving into the nearest ditch.

Of all the differences between our two cultures, I find the general French attitude to driving the most inexplicable. On any road journey in Britain, one will encounter thoughtless, incompetent and sometimes stupidly dangerous drivers. In our part of France, at least half the motorists seem to be either drunk, drugged, mentally deranged, or simply have a pressing death wish. Quite often, it seems that the drivers I meet are in the grip of all these conditions at the same time. What, of all their antics, enrages me most about the worst drivers is that they always signal carefully with their indicators before committing a particularly insane manoeuvre.

This year's road death figures for France have just been announced, and they are more than twice as high as the British tally. Given that their country is twice the size of ours with only the same number of people travelling around it, this statistic has to say something about comparative standards of driving. Last year at this time, I saw a television programme featuring a panel of everyday French motorists being asked about their views on the annual carnage, and what they thought of their own levels of ability and attitudes. All calmly confessed to the most horrendous habits, admitted that the figures were a national disgrace, then agreed with a mutual shrug that they would not be changing their ways in the foreseeable future.

Feeling pleased with myself after shouting in patois at an overtaking Parisian that he should go back to his own country, I tune to a BBC radio station and listen to a programme about obsessive behaviour. The first speaker is a man who feels he must spin twenty times in each direction every morning to maintain symmetry in the universe. He is followed by a woman who apologises to her left shoe for putting the other one on first. Another lady describes a gripping compulsion to clench her right buttock while driving past oncoming traffic, or the left cheek when overtaking parked cars or street lamps. After thinking that she would get all the buttock-clenching moments she could care for just by venturing on to the roads around Bricquebec on market day, I reflect on how good it is to know that there are still some interestingly eccentric people in the United Kingdom. And that, in spite of what most Normans seem to think, they have not all come to live over here.

Arriving at what is claimed by the town's tourist association to be the biggest square in all Normandy (if not all France), I set about looking for a parking space.

Hundreds of cars will be lining every street and alleyway around the market, but not one of them will be blocking off a garage, driveway or pedestrian passage. Most will be parked quite illegally on pavements, stretches of grass, flowerbeds or awkward bends, but common interest means that drivers don't break the unwritten rules. If they did and the authorities applied the official parking canons, the market would simply cease to exist. Tolerance is the French character trait I most admire, and their pragmatic attitude to adapting or getting round the rules comes a close second. If the French don't like a law, they simply pretend it doesn't exist. This is probably why so many British people are worried about entering Europe more fully. Britons complain bitterly about any new law or regulation which they think unjust or unnecessary, but in general will observe it. They also believe with good reason that the French will not. One truism I have learned in my years in Normandy is that national stereotypes generally have much more than a grain of truth about them. This is the reason, of course, that they have become stereotypes.

Of all the markets in the peninsula, Bricquebec is the most well-attended and, for me, the most appealing. The weekly fair is staged around the ancient castle where William the Conqueror, Queen Victoria, Rommel and sometimes even Lord Lucan are claimed to have been guests, though not all at the same time. What started centuries ago as a livestock market is now awash with stalls offering anything from field-fresh farm produce to second-hand chain saws, saucy underwear and very obviously imitation Rolex watches. Most importantly and regardless of what is on offer, the weekly gathering of thousands of local people also gives them the chance to catch up with all the latest gossip within a thirty-kilometre circumference.

Although the livestock section of the market is close by, I decide it would be rude not to visit my Bricquebec local first, so drop in to the *Café de Paris* to catch up on what has been happening during my absence overseas.

Inside, it is standing-room only, and as I breathe in the familiar mixture of industrial-strength tobacco fumes and interesting body odours, I see that we have visitors from the more remote parts of the Cotentin peninsula. Some of these sturdy folk are standing at the bar, though at first glance appear to be sitting down.

I have often observed the curious phenomenon that the further people live away from the towns and villages in our part of Normandy, the shorter and wider they usually are. Perhaps that is why they call our region Lower Normandy. For whatever reason, the really rural inhabitants of the Cotentin peninsula are usually close to the earth in more ways than one, and often seem to be as broad as they are tall. As the locals say, they are *trapu*. In England I am of average height and what the health police would call clinically obese, but in some company on market day in Bricquebec, I am a comparatively willowy giant.

Lunchtime is approaching, and as the *Café de Paris* serves no food, many of the customers are warming-up with a snack before going in search of a proper meal. Jammed in one corner, I see a family of six obvious out-of-towners working with almost grim determination on a mountain of chips and fiery *merguez* sausages bought from the stall outside. They are also giving a fascinating demonstration of the French ability to eat, drink, talk, smoke and gesticulate at the same time without appearing to draw breath.

After all my time in bars across France, I still feel self-conscious about eating food not bought on the premises, but here, the custom is almost universally acceptable, even when taken to extremes. I recently saw a family setting out a comprehensive picnic on the terrace of a local bar, and they quite unconcernedly asked the owner for plates and knives and condiments in return for buying a bottle of wine. I have not yet seen a customer setting up a barbecue outside or even inside the *Café de Paris*, but it would not surprise me greatly.

When we have completed the formalities of exchanging kisses and polite enquiries about our families, relations, pets and livers, Madame Collette explains that Freddo has gone out to buy her mother a birthday present. Although she does not say so, we both know her husband will also be dropping in on all the other bars in the town to sample their variety of house wine, and to check that they are not taking as much money as the *Café de Paris*.

Collette's mother bustles past with her ancient broom, pausing only to tell me how unfit, unwell and scruffy I look. *Maman* is almost ninety, but still works from dawn till late every day of the week keeping the premises clean and the customers in order. I sometimes think what it must have been like, sixty years ago, for her to look through the window and watch a German officer strutting across the square for his morning brandy, or to fend off the advances of a drunken soldier on payday. It is strange to think that the occupation of France and those somehow unreal scenes we see in grainy old newsreel films happened right here, and for *Maman*, within a working lifetime.

My thoughts are interrupted as the patron of the *Café de Paris* makes his return, waving proudly the gift he has bought at the hardware stall by the castle gate. We shake hands as he makes a ribald comment about my grey hairs, and I say I am glad to see him looking well, though I notice his face has become even more florid. The glowing intensity of Freddo's cheeks and nose are a talking point even in a town where a ruddy visage is not uncommon, and, as with the official moustache-growing stakes, there is said to be an informal competition amongst some members of the drinking fraternity to see who can develop and nurture the most striking facial hue. An apocryphal story has it that Freddo once lingered at the crossroads outside the bar, and all the traffic stopped till he moved on. This is not a very plausible story, as there are no traffic lights in the town, and even if there were, I can think of few local drivers who would take any notice of them, especially when they were on red.

After buying him a drink to top up his bloodstream and colour, I compliment Freddo on his choice of a birthday present for his mother-in-law, and say I am sure she will be pleased with her new broom. We talk about what has been happening in our lives, and when I ask him how best to look after the goose that has arrived at La Puce, he is happy to instruct me. The local methods of approach vary, he says, but he has perfected what is generally accepted as the most effective treatment. Firstly, I must win the bird's trust by giving it affectionate words and generous helpings of corn. Then, when it is eating contentedly, I should creep up from behind with a pair of freshly sharpened garden shears. Just where the body meets the neck is the best place, and a single snip will usually do the trick.

By now, an enthusiastic audience has gathered, and advice on the best way to kill, clean and cook Ermintrude is offered from all sides. When I explain that my wife says our gift from heaven is not for eating, an incredulous silence falls, and the patron of the *Café de Paris* orders a large brandy to get over the shock. He should know by now, he says, just how incomprehensible is the English attitude to animals which were born to be enjoyed on a plate, but it still takes some believing that even the residents of the Mill of the Flea intend keeping a goose as a family pet.

Calling at the livestock market, I turn down the offer of a three-legged sheep at a special discount price, and watch two schoolchildren making a fuss of a trayload of ducklings as their mother haggles with the stallholder. The girls are squealing with delight at the antics of the furry bundles as they pick them up and cuddle them tenderly. Over the coming months, they will enjoy helping feed and rear the birds, then, when Christmas arrives, they will just as happily help kill and dress their playmates for the table. Like them, I see no contradiction in this. Unlike many people today, the two little girls know exactly where their food comes from. Perhaps more importantly, they will know that their little cuddly ducklings had the best possible lives before arriving on the plate.

Though there are a whole variety of birds on sale at the livestock market, none seem to fit my wife's precise requirements, and after a fruitless hour searching for a mate for Ermintrude I am told by a man with a very talkative chicken under his arm that I should pay a call on the Birdwoman of Bricquebec. Of all the traders, she is the most likely to have what I am looking for. Knowing her and where she comes from, he says after looking around nervously, she may even have a magic goose which will be able to lay a golden egg.

I laugh politely at his joke, thank him and his chicken for the advice, and stroll through the castle grounds to the unofficial market, which is today taking place in the shadow of the towering castle keep, or *donjon*. Although we have been quite adept at stealing words from the French over the centuries, in this case we made a poor choice. The old French word for underground cells or what we would call dungeons is the much more evocative *oubliette*, which comes from the verb 'to forget'.

As well as the official stallholders, there are always people with something to sell who cannot afford or do not wish to pay for a pitch. By tradition, the casual traders will wait until the market inspector has made his rounds and checked that nobody is stealing a centimetre of ground more than they have paid for, then move in and set up shop in any convenient space. Many will be from the remoter reaches of the giant marsh that bisects the peninsula, and their isolation and alleged lifestyles set them apart at market as well as in local society. The *maraisais* seem, on the whole, to be perfectly normal, but some are alleged by the more superstitious country people to have mysterious powers. It is also somewhat unkindly said that when a typical marsh-dweller introduces you to his wife and sister, he is more than likely to be accompanied by only one woman.

At the castle keep, I see the usual miscellany of animals, farm produce and unwanted household goods laid out on the pavement, and find myself drawn to a glass eye which stares unwaveringly at me from the top of a folding table. Also on offer alongside the eye are an ancient hearing aid, a pair of glasses with one lens masked by tape, a set of yellowing dentures and a wooden leg, complete with straps made from what looks like the remains of an old horse harness.

I ask the woman sitting behind the table if the items are by any chance related, and she explains that they were her husband's, but he has no use for them as he passed away over the weekend. Rather than bury them with him, she has saved the gravediggers considerable work, and is now hoping that someone at the market may be in need of one or more of the valuable accessories. Rather optimistically, I feel, she tells me she is really hoping that someone will pass by who needs all the appliances, and she will be able to sell them on as a job lot and finally put all memories of her husband to rest. At this, the woman on the next stall observes that anyone in the position to need all the spare parts on offer would also be in no fit state to pass by, let alone see the goods or hear her advertising slogans. As unpleasantness seems about to break out, I offer my condolences to the new widow, refuse her helpful suggestion that I buy the prosthetics at a bargain price for possible future use, and am eventually directed to where the Birdwoman of Bricquebec has set out her stall.

A tiny, nut-brown woman of indeterminate age, she is sitting on an old wicker chair, and, after the build-up from the man with the chatty chicken, I am disappointed to see that she is reading the racing page of the local paper rather than casting runes or bewitching the occasional passer-by. On her head, she wears a lace cap of the type I last saw in a Memories of Normandy exhibition at the town hall. At her feet are a collection of cardboard boxes which occasionally twitch and emit shrill beeps and squawks. In between these extremities and despite the warmth of the day, the lady is swathed in a heavy shawl, and the rest of her traditional clothing sits quite oddly with the pair of modern training shoes poking out beneath her long black dress. I explain my situation, and ask if she has by any chance a mature male goose in good condition, of friendly disposition, and preferably with a taste for classical music.

Happily, it seems the Birdwoman has just the animal I am looking for, and she reaches immediately for one of the larger boxes. I am no expert on geese, but the bird she produces looks not unlike Ermintrude, has the right number of webbed feet, and a large bill of the correct colour. I pretend to be a specialist in the breed and ask to examine its teeth so I can judge its age and condition, but she says she must not release the elastic band around its beak as its honking may alert the market inspector that illicit business is being done.

After a spirited haggling session, I settle for a price that would have got me the bird served up with full trimmings in the best restaurant in Cherbourg, and money changes hands. Ermintrude's potential mate does not seem too pleased at the prospect of joining me for the journey back to La Puce, so I ask about a carrying cage and am charged fifty francs for the cardboard box and a piece of old string with which to hobble the bird's legs. I finally persuade the goose back in the carton, and as I am about to leave, the Birdwoman nods conspiratorially towards her training shoes and pulls the hem of her dress away to reveal four small, muddy-brown birds. They are, she says, a very rare breed of duck found only in the *marais*. They are also renowned for their intelligence, good looks and taste. Moreover, they are all members of the same family, and orphans in search of a good and caring home. She can hardly bear to part with the hapless brood, and had intended taking them back to her cottage to raise as pets. But she can tell that I am an animal lover, and knows that they would be happier with me. They are still too young to fly, and when grown, will give us an endless supply of delicious duck eggs at no cost. They will also be good company for the goose.

As a final pitch, the Birdwoman adds that they also make delicious eating, and promises to give me an old and very special marsh-dwellers' recipe for duck and heron *pâté*.

I hesitate, then think of how pleased my wife will be with an additional family of refugees to care for. More money changes hands, and I tactfully turn away as the Birdwoman says a near-tearful goodbye to her orphan ducks before charging me another fifty francs for the box in which they are sitting.

Back at The Flea, I hand over the noisy cardboard boxes to my wife, remember aloud that I have forgotten to buy any animal feed, and say I will have to return to the market. Engrossed with getting to know the new members of our extended family, my wife nods absent-mindedly, and I am free to escape to the village and the weekly meeting of the Jolly Boys Club of Néhou.

Men use thought only to conceal their injustices, and speech only to conceal their thought.

François Voltaire, French writer and phisosopher (1694-1778).

TWO

Outside the Bar Ghislaine, the collection of old cars, mopeds, tractors and other more unusual items of mobile agricultural equipment shows that today's meeting will be well attended. Most of the members of our informal association would have been in the bar at this time anyway, but today we have an official excuse for whiling away the afternoon.

If there were such a thing, Néhou would be most people's idea of a typical Norman village. With a population of around three hundred if all the outlying farms and habitations are included, the village proper consists of an imposing church with an immaculately kept graveyard around which is clustered a handful of weathered stone cottages. Other homes with mostly neatly kept gardens and windowsills displaying the inevitable pots of red geraniums line the crossroads over which the elevated church has looked for almost a thousand years.

Apart from Madame Ghislaine's bar and grocery store, the only two commercial enterprises in the village are a restaurant which seems more often closed than open (sometimes even at mealtimes), and a garage. Apart from frequent crash repairs, the garage specialises in maintaining and repairing all varieties of the ubiquitous *mobylette*, the most economical and therefore most popular form of transport in rural France. These sturdy mopeds will buzz their way happily up most hills, cover more than a hundred miles for every five litres of *mélange* in the tank, and have been known to tow tractors out of trouble in the rainy season. With the addition of a trailer, they can also carry family members and most animals up to the size of a small cow.

I park our elderly Volvo estate in front of the church, and walk towards the familiar brown door with its notices of once-special occasions and advertisements for long-forgotten products.

Alongside the bar is the grocery shop, and alongside that is the length of rusty guttering, metal piping and selection of old enamel cigarette posters which together form the village *pissoir*.

Things change even in rural Normandy, but against all the odds, the redoubtable Madame Ghislaine's bar and grocery store is still open for business. Once upon a time, every village in France would have its own general store, always run by a woman, and often with a bar alongside.

With the arrival and spread of supermarkets offering goods at less than the price a village shopkeeper would have to pay for them, an institution was doomed. This is more than simply the inevitable march of progress, because, just as in Britain, the village store was and is always much more than somewhere to buy your groceries. Along with the village hall, the local *épicerie* was the original rural community centre, and the focal point for every village. Now, Néhou is the only village in our immediate area with both a grocery store and a bar. I am ashamed to admit that, like the majority of people in the neighbourhood, we do most of our shopping in the local supermarket, but in my small way I try my best to help keep the Bar Ghislaine afloat by drinking as much as possible when I am on the premises. It would be a minor but significant tragedy if our village lost its bar and grocery store, and we would also lose our club debating rooms. As a member said to me the other day, it is not easy to have a philosophical conversation about Life in the cold meat aisle at the local Super U.

Squeezing my way into the bar, I see that we have a full house for today's meeting. The precise number of JBC members is unknown as there are no club records, or secretary to keep them. Broadly, any male who lives in or near the village, was alive at the time of the D-Day landings and likes to smoke, drink and talk a lot is a life member. Exceptions are made for younger villagers of exceptional talent like JayPay, our local superchef and sole entry this year for the moustache-growing championship of all Normandy. Providing they are prepared to pay the entry fee of at least two full rounds of drinks per session, outsiders are always welcome to join in the proceedings, and even foreigners like me may be granted a special overseas membership if they put their hand in their pocket at regular intervals and agree to keep quiet when wiser men talk. There is, however, not a pocket in the world deep enough to allow its owner to join our club if he comes from St Jacques, our rival village on the other side of the crossroads. The only other local people not made welcome at our meetings are teetotallers and women. The lack of female membership is not so much due to any deep-rooted misogyny, but because few women apart from Madame Ghislaine ever choose to pass through the bead-curtained doorway between bar and grocery store. The general feeling is that they hear quite enough rubbish from idle and foolish men at home, so there is no need to go shopping for more.

Our most senior member and lifetime president is Old Pierrot, who claims to have lived in the area since before the church and village were built, and to have been around when the French sensibly fought the English to the exclusion of virtually all other enemies, with bows and arrows and pikes as the weapons of choice. Whatever his real age and provenance,

Old Pierrot (we have a Young Pierrot who only began to claim his state pension a decade or so ago) allegedly lives with a flock of raven familiars somewhere outside the village in the more distant reaches of the *marais*. This great flood plain is a place of isolated and sometimes haunting beauty, and remains untouched by the changing world. To be there when the mist falls on the marshlands and the notorious Cotentin wind howls, it is not difficult to imagine the times when even Old Pierrot was young, and life was hard indeed. Nowadays, many villagers spend their evening in front of the television, but old men still like to sit and recall past adventures, and a meeting of the Jolly Boys Club is one of the rare events where I prefer to listen rather than talk.

Inside our clubroom, last winter's log still lies sulking in the hearth of the vast Norman fireplace, and the walls remain a pleasing shade of nicotine. The space behind the bar counter is at least twice the size of the area provided for customers, and the small and eclectic huddle of bottles on the back shelf are a good walk away from the serving-point. This is not because Madame Ghislaine is trying to prevent us from helping ourselves while she attends to business in the shop, or that she is trying to dissuade her customers from drinking. Nor is it because our hostess wishes to maintain a distance between herself and her exclusively male customers, or, as some club members have alleged, that she is trying to edge us off the premises by gradually shifting the bar towards the door. It is simply that it was moved more than three years ago so that her husband Bernard could start redecorating the room, and he has not got round to it yet.

As usual on club days, the curtains have been drawn to give us privacy, and also so that we will not be reminded that it is a beautiful day and thus risk feeling guilty that we are hiding from it. In spite of the gloom, there are no lights on, which is normal practice in many rural Norman shops and households at this time of the afternoon and year. Electricity, as the local expression has it, is expensive, and daylight is free.

My eyes becoming accustomed to the gloom, I am pleased to see that most of my closest friends are in attendance. At one end of a long bench reserved for committee members, the massive JayPay is resting his belly on a low stool, and equilibrium is maintained at the other end by another heavyweight member of the community. Hubert Adouard approaches JayPay in physical stature and presence, and is another moustache specialist, though it is generally agreed that his huge and flamboyant creation lacks the subtle style and nuance to have warranted entry in this year's competition. The exact time and venue for the regional heats of the moustache-growing championship have yet to be formalised, but the build-up to the grand final in Rouen will be as keenly followed as any other sporting event in the area and beyond. Betting will be heavy and rivalry intense, especially between our village and St Jacques, and extreme measures taken to prevent cheating, or even sabotage. Fans of the competition still talk of the time when a leading contender was nobbled by a rival who offered him a light for his cigarette, and then deliberately set fire to his heavily beeswaxed moustache. As the day of the final approaches and tension runs high, some competitors sleep behind locked doors and wear special moustache masks to prevent a sudden attack, and at the same time conceal the true size and style of their entry. I have been told that the St Jacques entrant in this year's event has been seen walking around with a sack over his head, but most of our villagers agree that, like a pop singer with a cucumber down his trouser front, he has little to hide and is only showing off to impress women fans.

Eventually finding a seat close to the bar, I see that, sandwiched in between our moustache-growing aficionados are two other members of roughly the same age, but completely different in their appearance, characters and mental processes. One is a true philosopher, while the other I find impossible to engage in a sensible conversation.

My thoughtful friend Jacques Délabré is a man of great intellect, experience and humanity, and like most people occupied more with the mind than the passing whims of fashion, cares little for his personal appearance. Winter and summer he is swathed in an army greatcoat of World War II vintage, held in place with a length of baling twine. A bachelor who lodges in a hamlet to the north of the village, he appears to gain his inspiration and nourishment solely from regular infusions of coarse red wine and the home-cured tobacco in his old pipe. Jacques travels everywhere on an upright bicycle which could well pre-date his overcoat, and because of this and a slight physical resemblance to the great French film director and actor, is referred to somewhat disrespectfully by my wife as Jack Tatty.

Alongside our resident philosopher is Peppi, a strange character who is obsessively interested in old American films, and who tries to talk to me in a weird mixture of Norman patois and memorable lines from classic Hollywood movies. This is not a comfortable combination, especially when the speaker is asking after my health while giving a very bad imitation of Humphrey Bogart playing Sam Spade in *The Maltese Falcon*.

After observing tradition by calling for a round of drinks, I learn that my friend and mentor René Ribet is away on urgent business with the Widow of Négreville, and that the current subject for debate is the comparative venality and level of corruption of politicians. The discussion has been prompted by the latest reports of fiscal irregularities at government level in France, and there is much amusement when I tell my friends about the fuss in the British media over a cabinet minister who was dismissed for allegedly lying about a phone call he may or may not have made. As Old Pierrot remarks, lying has always been an important part of any politician's job, and even a basic qualification in countries where the electorate takes a realistic view of life and human frailty. Few French voters could have confidence in a representative who was even suspected of telling the truth at all times.

The conversation then moves on to a more general discussion on subjective truth, and our club philosopher proposes that the downfall of man was not set in motion by the mere eating of an apple, but by the arrival and development of language. Animals, he points out, cannot lie to each other because they cannot speak. Body language is all-revealing, as it must have been with humans before we learned to communicate with words. Once, we had the power to know what others were thinking just by looking at them, but the moment he was able to speak, Man was also able to deceive. A sad reflection on the human race, Jacques concludes, is that we do it so well.

It is now time for my summary of news from abroad, and a report in my copy of the weekly *Telegraph* helps confirm the club's belief that those who make and enforce the laws in Britain have a strange idea of justice. My story concerns a baker who is to be prosecuted under our race relations provisions for advertising his long loaves as 'English sticks', and declaring on a poster that they are much better than the French variety. Secure in their certainty that French bread is the best in the world, my friends are unperturbed by such an obviously ludicrous claim, and bemused that the man is to be prosecuted for a race relations offence. Clearly, it is unanimously agreed, a much more suitable charge for an English baker attempting to make eatable *baguettes* would be one of criminal damage.

At this point, our debate is interrupted by the arrival of a dense cloud of pungent cigarette smoke, from which eventually emerges a small and ashen-faced figure. Our postman is officially a foreigner as he lives within infectious distance of the centre of St Jacques, but is granted special membership as he is a man of some importance in the area. Apart from his occupation giving him early access to local scandals, he delivers all benefit and welfare cheques, and, more importantly, determines how promptly they arrive. Patrick the Post's round changes daily, and depends more on who is in or out of favour than logical geographical progression. It is common knowledge that, since they fell out over the price of a pork chop, the butcher at St Jacques receives his mail up to a week late, and he is Patrick's next-door-neighbour.

While we await his excuse for delivering himself late to an important club meeting, Patrick composes himself by absent-mindedly finishing off my glass of wine, then goes through his trademark ritual of rolling a cigarette while peering through the haze of smoke rising from the one already in his mouth. Finally satisfied it is of perfect shape and consistency, he lights the fresh cigarette after discarding the stub of the old one, and tells us his dramatic tale.

Rising before first light as usual, he had, he said, dressed in the dark for fear of waking his wife. As we will all know, this was not so much out of consideration for her beauty sleep, but from fear of her insatiable sexual appetite. Our postman's wife is as generously proportioned as he is slight, and Patrick believes Madame Megére makes continual and completely unreasonable demands on his vitality. Besides, as he says, they already have two children, so there would be little point in further congress.

Pausing only to prepare another cigarette, our storyteller explains how, after dressing in the dark, he wiped his spectacles, put on his official hat, then walked into the kitchen to discover he had gone almost blind overnight. All he could see through his spectacles was a blur. There is a sharp intake of breath, silence falls on the room, and the members lean forward in rapt attention. Being French, most of our club members are complete hypochondriacs, so this is gripping stuff. Patrick is also much practiced at detailing all the grisly aspects of any new ailment, as he has collected more exotic illnesses than anyone in the area with the exception of the legendary Michel le Scabieuse, who has had whole medical books written about him. Sadly, Scabby Michael is too ill to attend today's meeting, but has sent a note of apology together with a full list of his latest and most cinematic afflictions.

After graphically describing his moments of blind terror, our storyteller rolls another cigarette to tease out the tale as artfully as the shreds of his home-made tobacco, and then reveals the cause of his sudden disability. He had not, thankfully, suffered a sudden and permanent blurring of vision. Mercifully, there was a much more mundane explanation.

Patrick having revealed the *dénouement,* a communal sigh of relief escapes from the parted lips of his audience, more drinks are ordered, and our next debate focuses on the dangers of blowing your nose and cleaning your spectacles with the same handkerchief.

Some hours later, and I have returned to La Puce, invigorated by our meeting and what it has taught me about my fellow man. Unfortunately, Donella's body language makes it clear that I am not in her good books. My excuse that the feed merchant had run out of feed and that I had to comb the area for a bag of maize is brushed aside as she tells me I have bought a pig in a poke; or more accurately, a duck instead of a goose. I have also bought probably the only duck in existence which is afraid of water. To make matters worse, the family of alleged orphan ducklings flew off and disappeared in the general direction of Bricquebec the moment they were released from their box.

I am led to the big pond, and we find the hydrophobic duck hiding under a tree on the far bank. To win favour with my wife, I decide to take unilateral action by picking the bird up and throwing it directly on to the soupy waters. Nature, I reason, will then take over, the duck will do what should come naturally to its species, and Donella will forgive me.

When the waves have subsided and the duck has surfaced, there is a sudden and dramatic reaction. It lets out an agonised squawk, rears up out of the water, then makes off across the surface with wings flapping frantically in an obvious attempt to take off. Like the giant seaplane designed by Howard Hughes, it is clearly too heavy to fly for more than a few seconds, and blunders across the water until crash-landing in a shower of feathers on the small island in the centre of the pond.

When calm has been restored, I am able to see the reason for the duck's fear of this particular stretch of water. The unfortunate creature has come under submarine attack from at least a dozen of our murderous goldfish, and perhaps even their dread leader.

We first put Psycho into the big pond five years ago after agreeing to take him from his owner, who said he had eaten her Siamese fighting fish and frightened the family cat away. She was also expecting a baby, and could not contemplate leaving her precious child in the same room as the fish tank.

During his time in the big pond, Psycho has sired several generations of outwardly normal goldfish, but all seem to have inherited his killer genes. Now that the muskrat has apparently eaten all our crayfish and moved on to other parts, the goldfish have obviously taken over as the new arch-beasts of the big pond. Rather than seeing the giant mallard as a threat, they see it as a meal. I am now faced with crossing the dangerous waters in our leaky skiff to ferry the duck to safety, while my wife shouts encouragement and throws stones at Psycho and his gang to provide covering fire.

Back on dry land, the duck is given its first of what will probably need to be many counselling sessions, while I am despatched to Bricquebec to find the Birdwoman and recover either the family of orphaned ducks, or the huge sum of money I so stupidly paid for them.

Despite the late hour, the official market is still doing brisk business, but most of the mobile traders have moved on. The lady selling her late husband's spare parts is still looking for one severely disabled customer (or several with the correct missing or non-functioning bodily parts), and tells me that the Birdwoman has flown. She was last seen boxing up three small ducks, which approached the town from an easterly direction, landed at her feet and then disappeared beneath her skirts. According to the other traders, the same thing happens every week.

I think about my options, then decide to spend some time at the *Café de Paris* while pondering on the best way to explain to my wife that I have been fooled into buying probably the only homing ducks in Normandy, if not all France.

All in all, it has been a strange day, even by our standards.

It is a little after midnight, and I am sitting on the well in the orchard, watching my wife cut grass by the light of a buttery full moon. Below us in the copse by the mill cottage, I hear the occasional rustle of foliage and odd shriek of terror. Cato is obviously at the height of her activity at this time of the lunar cycle, and I feel for any shrews, mice or foxes unlucky enough to cross her path. Any poachers unwise enough to trespass on our terrain under a full moon must take their chances of surviving an encounter with our family pet, which I have long suspected to be the result of some past union between a standard tabby and a werewolf.

Far away at the big pond, the nervous duck will be hiding under the giant gunnera bush, and Gert and Daisy the escapologist chickens are hopefully still under lock and key in the hut by the stream. Ermintrude the goose is safely bedded down in the grotto, perhaps dreaming of taking the lead role in *Swan Lake*. Earlier today I played her a selection from my *Rock and Roll Blockbusters from the Fabulous Fifties* cassette, but she does not seem to care for the more modern classics. Donella is still obviously concerned that Ermintrude has not been found a life companion, and is proposing that we take her to market next week so she can select her own mate. I had a call from a South African travel writer friend last week, and he said his wife is very much like mine when it comes to animals. He recalled that, when they moved home, she insisted on taking their flock from Pietmaritzburg to Ladysmith in the family car. It was, he said, an interesting experience to have other drivers draw level and come eye-to-eye with a family of Toulouse geese sitting contentedly on the back seat of an elderly Morris Minor.

He added rather glumly that he later gave the car away rather than face the prospect of cleaning it, and that they had to spend the night camping out at the mid-point of the journey as the hotel they had booked had reservations about accommodating a gaggle of geese in the Winnie Mandela suite.

I am distracted by a ghostly white figure, and see that our barn owl is starting its nightly rounds. It is obviously unconcerned by Donella's presence, and lands on a broken fence post to watch as she strims around the base of one of the more upright apple trees. When she moves away, the owl rises from the post, hovers for a heartbeat, and then falls surprisingly awkwardly to the cleared ground. Almost instantly, it lifts off with a casual beat of powerful wings, a small shrew struggling frantically in its talons. For the owl and its family, it has been a rewarding encounter. For the shrew it is the illest of meetings by moonlight.

The occasional car passes as my wife begins to attack the forest of thistles beneath the giant cedar tree at the far end of the orchard, so I know our nocturnal gardening session will be common knowledge in the village tomorrow. Together with her decision to cut grass at midnight, there will be the additional talking points that Donella is wearing waist-length waders, a boiler suit buttoned up to her neck, and a stocking mask made from a pair of laddered tights.

The reason for the nocturnal mowing is that Old Pierrot has told her that grass mown under a full moon will grow more slowly. He said it was a tip passed on to him by the original designer of the gardens at Versailles, who must have known a thing or two about lawns. The reason my wife is dressed like a particularly nervous beekeeper is that, ironically, she is a magnet to not only all species of animals in search of a free and luxurious billet, but also to every type of insect that bites or stings. While I am seemingly immune to attack from the midges that hold a world-wide convention at La Puce every summer, they seem to queue up to feast on Donella.

Nobody seems to know what makes some types of human blood especially attractive to biting insects, and over the years we have tried every sort of modern and traditional repellent. Last year, my wife covered herself with a very expensive ointment said to keep even the giant yellow fever mosquito at bay, but it actually seemed to attract the attention of every malicious insect in the region.

Watching my wife working in the moonlight I think of how content she is to be here, and remember my mother sitting in the orchard one late autumn day, wrapping apples for the winter store. When I complained about some petty disagreement with my wife, my mother said that I should count our many blessings, and make the best use of every day together at La Puce. Time, she said, leaks away, and it is always tomorrow when you realise how good yesterday was.

At nearly eighty, my mother looked at least ten years younger, and people would say how beautiful and full of grace she was, and how surprised they were that I could be her son. She was a dancer in her younger days, and her party trick at more than seventy was to perform a series of dazzlingly effortless high kicks, followed by a full splits. When I was a teenager, she showed me a photograph of her receiving the winner's cup in a seaside beauty competition, and I remember how stupidly surprised I was that she could have once been so young. She loved to visit us at La Puce, and would talk about coming to stay with us for the rest of her days when the time was right. That would not be while my father was alive, as he would never consider living with us, and almost even worse, in a foreign country. Then, quite suddenly, my agelessly beautiful mother became old and frail. She never complained, but the sparkle left her eyes, and I knew that her every day was full of pain. We left La Puce two years ago, when she called to say she was missing us but did not feel up to the journey across the Channel. As we sat on the ferry watching Cherbourg disappear in the early morning haze, we knew we would not return until my mother was well again, or the worst happened. Although we never spoke of it, I think we both knew that she would not recover. It was not just out of duty that we returned to England, but because I loved my mother and knew I would not be able to face losing her while we were apart.

She was in great pain for more than a year, but her spirit was indomitable. Every morning, I would go with her to the shops near her home, and sometimes the journey would take an hour, but she would insist on walking. Once, I tried to persuade her to take a stick, but she said she didn't want people to see her looking like a little old lady. Then we stopped making the daily trip, and when the ambulance arrived to take her to hospital, I knew she would never leave that place.

On our last day together, I kissed her cheek and she held me and told me how much she loved me and what a good boy I had been, and that I must look after my family and treasure our time together. When I got up to leave, our eyes met and I knew that she was silently asking me if it would be alright for her to leave the pain behind. I nodded, then sat and held her hand till she fell to sleep.

I had to tell my father that his wife of more than sixty years had left us, and it was the first time I had seen him cry. He never forgave himself for not going to see her in the hospital, and for months, he raged against my mother for leaving him, and me for telling him she had gone.

Amongst other keepsakes, we have brought my mother's favourite easy chair to La Puce. I am not ashamed to say I see her sitting there and talk to her every morning. I know it is fanciful, but I believe she is still with us and always will be, and the thought comforts me in bad times.

Estragon: Charming spot. Inspiring prospects. Let's go.
Vladimir: We can't.
Estragon: Why not?
Vladimir: We're waiting for Godot.

Waiting for Godot (Act I).

THREE

The darling buds of May have come early to the Mill of the Flea, and I have been dining with tigers.

Though Bricquebec is the biggest town in our area, as residents at Néhou we are part of the canton of St-Sauveur-Le-Vicomte. With a population of three thousand living in or around the town, St Sauveur has a mostly ruined castle, a nearby forest, a sizeable river running through it, and sits beside the great stretch of marshlands that bisect the Cotentin peninsula. Apart from that, it is an unremarkable though solid and honest Norman town, with its own homespun appeal.

Like many other market towns in France, St Sauveur has seen hard times in recent years. Now that, as many local people believe, the small farming industry has been destroyed by the European common agricultural policy, St Sauveur is looking increasingly towards tourism for its salvation, and makes every effort to appeal to visitors with money to spend. Amongst the attractions, there is a campsite in the castle grounds, an impressive abbey on the outskirts, and holidaymakers can try their hands at canoeing along the *Douve* past the old milk factory, or look around the museum dedicated to the town's most famous son.

The writer Jules Barbey d'Aurevilly is said to be the Norman equivalent of Robert Louis Stevenson, but as none of his books have been translated into English, I cannot tell if this is a fair comparison, and I have never met any Frenchman who has read any of his works. I have even heard cynics from other towns in the area claim that Barbey never existed, and that he was invented to give St Sauveur something to boast about, but this is obviously jealousy on their part. He is clearly highly thought of locally, and even the public toilets are named for him.

Last week, the main event to attract visitors was a fair to celebrate milk in all its variety and splendour, and soon there is to be another exhibition of Norman lace hats across the ages. The latest sign of St Sauveur's attempts to appear more cosmopolitan is the pizzeria in the high street, and most of the townspeople hope it will be a success. The pizza house (which is not named after Barbey d'Aurevilly) is on the site of a discount clothing store, which was obviously not offering enough discount and closed last year. With so many grander and longer-established tourist attractions in the region, it will not be easy for St Sauveur to become a tourist honeypot, but our little town is doing its best, and learning to adapt to what visitors from other parts of France and Europe think they want when spending their holiday money.

Turning off the main road into the town this afternoon, I made sudden eye-to-eye contact with a large Bengal tiger sitting glumly on the back of a lorry, and realised with a twinge of disappointment that all the people lining the roads were not waiting to welcome their living local writer. Nowadays in Britain, a travelling show with animals would be refused a licence by most local authorities. Here, any *cirque* is more than welcome, and the lions, tigers and other performers paraded proudly around the streets before the evening performance.

After waving half-heartedly at a number of spectators who seemed to think I or my ancient car were part of the entertainment, I managed to escape the convoy and find a space outside the Bar Despond as the procession pulled up in the square. A healthy crowd had gathered to see the fun, and the tigers were clearly the main attraction. Seen close-up they were magnificent creatures, but apart from giving the odd growl, the family seemed more interested in going to sleep than eating anyone. Even so, the chicken wire keeping them apart from the public seemed very fragile, and would have made the average British health and safety busybody go into severe trauma. I like the way that French parents are much less fussily protective about their children than in Britain, but still winced when a man lifted a small boy up to the lorry and encouraged him to put his fingers through the wire and offer the largest tiger a piece of his *croissant*. Fortunately, the beast was not hungry.

Smiling vacuously at a handful of children who were obviously disappointed that my old Volvo had not exploded in the usual way of a circus clown's car, and were now looking at me as if trying to decide if I was the Wild Man of Borneo or the Fattest Man on Earth, I went into the Bar Despond to upset the patron by ordering a coffee and a smile to be served outside.

Mr Morne is the fifth owner to try and make a go of the business in as many years, and to be fair he does not have much to smile about. Although he is the boss, I knew he would not be unhappy to play the waiter and bring my coffee out to the pavement, as there is a small surcharge for the service; but he would be very unhappy that I had taken the liberty of ordering my drink from inside the bar.

It is inarguable that French waiters - and waitresses - are amongst the best in the world, and unlike their British counterparts, do not seem to see the work as demeaning. But over the years I have observed that there are strict and unspoken rules of engagement between servers and served in France, and I had just broken one of the most important. Apart from his speed and manual dexterity, any waiter can show how accomplished he is by the level of his ability to spot a customer in need of food or drink anywhere on the premises, even at the busiest times. In the complex rules of the waiting game, status is gained if the customer is very small and sitting unobtrusively outside in a remote area of the terrace, or even better, completely out of sight of the waiter's patrol area. To test out their reputations, I have deliberately played hide-and-seek with some of the best waiters in the business, and have been asked for my order even while pretending to be looking in the shop window next door.

On the darker side, the unwritten rule that the customer waits for the waiter can also be used to show what the server thinks of his prospective client, or of humanity in general. The owner of the Bar Despond is a dedicated misanthrope, and had I not told him I wanted a coffee, I could still have been sitting at my table when the circus packed up and left town.

As the roustabouts began their work, I watched a young man try to lead a llama across the square. When it stopped and lay down, he yanked on its tether, and when that had no effect, kicked it repeatedly in the side. Eventually, the beast gave a resigned grunt, got up and followed its keeper unresentfully to where the big tent was being raised. In Britain, a posse of animal lovers would probably have attacked the man, but here, no one seemed to object to or even notice his casual act of cruelty. Nobody is kinder to their pets than the French, and when I used to take my dog into a bar on a hot day, the owner would invariably bring a bowl of water and make a fuss of him. Sometimes, I would be chided for not asking for Lucky's drink before my own. Perversely, I frequently see farm animals treated badly, and sometimes very cruelly. This rigid distinction between pets and working animals and how they should be cared for is another singular example of how the French differ

- or appear to differ - from the British.

The llama having spat indifferently at a nearby child and limped away, the crowd suddenly parted, and I was pleased to see my good friend Coco career across the square in his customised Land Rover. Like his bar, it is painted an interesting purple. It also bears the scars of many an encounter with trees, other vehicles and the odd unwary pedestrian, and has the words *Impossible Mission* painted on the rear. According to some customers, this is a statement of Coco's view of life, but I prefer to think it is a warning to any driver foolish enough to try and overtake him. From the plimsoll line of mud around the upper bodywork, I could see that the Land Rover's owner had been indulging his passion for exploring the normally inaccessible areas of the marshlands surrounding the town.

Though he looks like a demented Old Testament prophet on a bad hair day, Coco Lecoq is in fact the most successful bar owner in St Sauveur. He is also a philosophical countryman and freethinker in the classic French mould. He is a man who understands nature and the realities of rural life, but knows there is more to be had from living by letting the mind range far and free.

Of all the bars in rural France that I have frequented across the years, the Flaming Curtains is the most unusual, and to me, one of the most attractive. The normally standard plastic and chromium plating bar décor and fixtures are missing, and the huge open fireplaces at the *Rideau Cramoisi* are real, and used for their proper purpose of heating in the winter and cooking all year round. The overall ambience of the heavily beamed and wood-panelled interior is enhanced by an eccentric variety of furnishings, which include artefacts from World War II, hand-carved sculptures, Coco's impressionist paintings, a monstrous plastic toothbrush hanging above the bar, and a somehow strangely incongruous string of paper Chinese lanterns. Customers' bicycles and mopeds are often brought into the bar, and also quite large engine parts when

Coco is overhauling his Land Rover and it is raining.

Although clients, dogs and passing ramblers are welcome to wander unchecked throughout the premises, the table in front of one of the fireplaces is reserved strictly for family use. Here, the couple's two young sons will spend an hour each evening doing their homework, and the family eats, laughs and occasionally argues very much in public, which adds to the feeling that you are visiting an eccentric friend's home rather than a commercial enterprise.

The clientele is as mixed as the décor, with farmers and smart-suited businesspeople rubbing shoulders at lunchtimes and, at some time during the week, virtually every young person living in and around the town will call in to the Flaming Curtains. The blackened cauldron in the fireplace next to the kitchen is in daily use, and Coco's wife Chantal is famed throughout the area for the quality of her traditional country dishes.

The Flaming Curtains is also unique in being the only bar I frequent where I need to negotiate the size of my bar bill at the end of each visit, and have to persuade the owners that I have drunk more and thus owe more than they claim. All bars in our area work on a tab system, but at Coco's bar, regulars keeps their own record of what they have consumed. Perhaps surprisingly to people who do not know the proprietor, his wife and their customers, this honour system seems to work perfectly well. I am usually the only one who causes a hiccup, as the debate on how much I have actually got through during a long session can become quite heated, and usually results in more drinks crossing the counter while we reach final agreement.

When he had put the owner of the Bar Despond in an even blacker mood by casually mentioning how much money the Flaming Curtains had taken during the previous week, Coco told me he had just bought the old house alongside his bar, and is to convert it into lodging rooms. He had recently seen a television programme about a hotel in New York which specialised in having bohemian artists and writers as guests, and he intends doing the same. He is sure that the venture will be a success, especially with the growing number of strange English people who appear in his bar and ask about accommodation in the area. Some say they are businessmen taking a long break from the pressures of making vast amounts of money across the Channel but are looking for really cheap lodgings; others say they are creative people not appreciated in their own country, and who have come to work and live in a more sympathetic environment.

Asked for an opinion, I told my friend I thought the idea would be an interesting experiment, as long as he makes sure to take the rents in advance. Over the years, an increasing number of expatriates have arrived in our area to make a new life, and many turn out to be unusual characters. Rather than the usual retired couples who appreciate the quality and pace of life in France, some new settlers in our area of Normandy seem to be on the run from someone or something, and sometimes even from themselves. Like the swallows, they tend to arrive in early summer, have ambitious ideas and what they believe will be enough money to see them through until they can make their schemes work. For most, the dreams of a golden summer soon fade to the harsh realities of a long, cold and hard-up winter.

Having heard Coco's plans for making the *Nouvelle Algonquin* a creative haven for fellow freethinkers, I told him I was going through a period of mourning for a significant loss. Donella has requisitioned my riverside shed as a home for our new chickens, so I now have nowhere to keep all the things I had collected just to keep in it. As I explained, British women seem to have no understanding of the almost mystic significance of this small retreat from the world, or of the value of the things a man likes to store in his shed. In our culture, I explained, even the most dilapidated hut can be a place of calm and security, where a husband can escape from his wife and the world, contemplate the meaning of life, and think about what and where he might have been had the dice of fate landed differently. An Englishman's garden shed is also a repository for all the things that a woman would throw away as useless, but that he knows might just come in useful one day. In my case, I had now to dispose of three perfectly good bags of cement, which became solid some years ago after I left them out in the rain.

To illustrate the significance of a private retreat to millions of British husbands, I told my friend about a man who lived in Kent, but had his shed in Normandy. To the casual observer, it might have looked like a derelict house, but to him it was his shed; somewhere he could relax, be himself and do exactly as he pleased.

A former publican, he had spent forty years working and living with his wife, and in all that time, the cellar of their pub was the only place where he could feel completely in charge of himself and his life. It was also the only place where he could smoke and drink without his wife knowing. When the couple retired, he missed the quietude of the cellar and asked permission to put up a small hut in the garden of their new home. His wife turned down his planning application on the grounds that it would spoil the view from her tasteful double-glazed gazebo, and matters grew worse when his daughter (who was quite like her mother in temperament) moved in with them after her husband ran off with a male friend.

After reading one of my books, the man wrote to thank me for giving him inspiration, and to say that he had persuaded his wife of the social advantages of being able to tell friends that they owned a *pied à terre* in Normandy. In spite of being a bad sea traveller and not liking France or the French or anywhere without pavements, the proposal had appealed to her snobbery, and she had picked an attractive but badly dilapidated house from the sheaf of agents' details he had collated. To his delight, she then fell in with the next stage of his plan, and allowed him to conduct all the negotiations, the viewing and the purchase. As she agreed, it would be better for him to visit Normandy frequently to arrange the renovations, and then when the last lick of paint had been applied, she could arrive and oversee the really important business of choosing the furniture and creating the overall ambience.

Two years on from the purchase, I visited the couple's holiday home, and was surprised to see it was still in a near-derelict condition. Inside the main room I found a single armchair in front of a rusty electric fire, and the walls lined with cartons of cigarettes, cases of whisky and trays of beer. Proudly, the owner told me that he had not lifted as much as a finger to improve the premises, and his wife was quite content to regularly inspect photographs of his allegedly painstaking restoration work. She was, he said, completely unaware that she was seeing photographs of someone else's house.

Opening two cans of beer, he explained that, on his first visit to the property, he had met a couple who were restoring a cottage in the next village, and as they beavered away he would make regular visits to take photographs of their progress. So far, the scheme was working perfectly. At last, he had his very own garden shed. It was a hundred miles away from his garden in England, but that meant it was also a hundred miles away from his wife and daughter. He knew he would have to face the music some day, and at the moment was having a problem in persuading the owners of the surrogate cottage to choose wallpaper and soft furnishings of which his wife would approve. One day, she would of course make the journey and all would be revealed, but he would cross that bridge when he came to it. For the moment, he was free to sit and think and smoke and drink to his heart's content in the peace and privacy of his own garden shed.

Returning to the subject of my waste disposal problem, I told a bemused Coco that I had spent the best part of the morning trying to say a rueful goodbye to my three bags of solidified cement.

In our early years in Normandy, each village had its own dump for unwanted household items, which was no more than a large hole in the ground at the end of a track well away from the nearest habitation. In those sensible times, the standard procedure was to back your car up to the edge of the pit and throw the unwanted items into it. Periodically, a man would appear on an earth-moving machine to fill the hole in and make a new one. Some skilful van drivers could manage the disposal operation without getting out of their vehicles by backing up to the very edge of the hole, slamming on the brakes then driving away at great speed. They still talk in our village about the local champion of this technique who went missing after telling his wife he was going to drop off some rubbish, and would be back in good time for dinner. It was a rainy afternoon in winter and he had taken at least one bottle of wine with his lunch, so some people believe he braked too late, disappeared into the hole and sank beneath a sea of rubbish shortly before the pit was filled in. For years afterwards, villagers would talk of strange sights and sounds on the anniversary of his disappearance, and having a possibly haunted rubbish tip gave our village significant status in the area. It is a good story, but having seen and heard his wife telling him what she thought of him, I suspect there may be a more prosaic reason for the man's disappearing act.

Often in the old days, a local *poubelle* would become almost a social centre, with people arriving to see what their neighbours were throwing away, and sometimes leaving with more than they had brought. I have even known of pitside parties, with friends agreeing to meet and combine business with pleasure by sharing a picnic. Then Brussels decided that the traditional system was a health hazard, and that every rubbish pit in rural France was to be filled in for the last time.

A weekly dustcart now does the rounds of our village, but the binmen will only take household refuse, or any items they either want for themselves or believe they can sell.

Knowing that even Norman dustmen would have no use for three solidified cement bags, I had loaded them in the car that morning, and set off to the village to find a suitable dumping ground. At the garage, the owner went through the breath-expelling, eye-rolling and shrugging routine usually reserved for customers wanting to know when their cars would be repaired, then called in his two mechanics, the woman who looks after the books, and a passing stranger. Nobody being able to come up with any ideas, we all retired to the Bar Ghislaine for further discussions.

When we came to live in the Norman countryside, I would become irritated when a simple query resulted in a full-blown drama of head-scratching analysis and debate, but soon learned there is a quite logical explanation for the tradition. In a rural backwater where little of great note happens on a daily basis, small matters take on significance beyond what busy city folk would think of as their merit. Also, most country-dwellers genuinely want to help their friends and neighbours, and by overblowing the scale of a problem, can feel pleased with themselves for helping solve it. Thus my three cement bags were destined to become a *cause célèbre*, and also the subject of a good story for those involved to relate during the long and tedious days of winter.

My journeying with the bags and how I eventually disposed of them also gives a fair example of the ambivalent French attitude to bureaucracy. Every French man or woman I know will complain regularly and bitterly about petty regulations. They will ignore them when it suits, but I believe they secretly enjoy setting up and dealing with convoluted procedures and transactions.

To buy a paving slab in our local garden centre, you must first go and wait in line to tell the girl at the checkout the colour and size you want. She will then look up the serial number in a ledger, and fill in a docket. You will then need to find a yard assistant, who will disappear to look in another ledger to see if what you want is currently in stock, even if you have explained that you have just seen a pile of them, or are actually standing next to or even on them.

When the assistant has put the ledger back on its shelf, he will watch as you load the slab in the back of the car, then make out another docket to prove you have had your goods. You must then return to the checkout, rejoin the queue and hand your *billet* to the girl. She will then consult another ledger to find the price. Finally, she will adjust the stock-control ledger, make out your receipt, take your money, and you will be free to leave if someone has not locked the gates in advance of the lunchtime closure. More complicated orders may require extra paperwork and procedure, and thus take a little longer.

Alternatively, you could just arrive, load the slab into your car and drive off with it, then settle the bill next time you drop in. In that case, nobody would have the slightest objection. In the same store, there is a long list of all the papers and certificates you will need to present in order to purchase a box of shotgun cartridges. In fact, the boxes are conveniently displayed on an open shelf next to the till, and customers in the queue will reach over and help themselves, much in the way of a mother picking up a packet of sweets for her child at the supermarket check-out.

All in all, it seems to me that creating a bureaucratic problem and then solving it by cutting corners is a sport which particularly appeals to the French psyche. Happily, it usually suits my mood, and who am I to try and change a national pastime?

Comfortably settled in the Bar Ghislaine and following several drinks, a reasoned debate and a number of telephone calls to acknowledged experts in the waste disposal field, it was generally agreed that my best move would be to take my problem and cement bags to the mayor of Néhou. Had, that is, he not been away on a goodwill hunting trip to the Alsace region. My only immediate solution, according to a quorum of the committee, would be to bury the bags on my own land, dump them on the land of an enemy, or take them to the special disposal centre at La-Haye-de-Puits, some twelve miles away. Of course, I would have to lie about where I live, as the tip there is only open to members of that commune. Another problem to be considered was what days and hours the *décheterie* was currently open to the public, and under what classification my solid cement bags would come so that I could ask for the right coloured docket at the gate.

Two hours later and I was queuing in a line of cars at the outer gates of the heavily defended tip. There were no armed guards or goon towers on the perimeter, but a high razor-wire fence surrounded the rows of colour-coded skips, presumably to prevent people either breaking in to deposit their illicit rubbish, or to steal somebody else's. Some years ago, I joined the wrong lane on the road going past the high-security nuclear recycling plant in the north of the peninsula, and sailed through the gates without a sign of interest from the security guards. Obviously, the authorities consider the protection of an unwanted three-piece suite more important than any threat to their collection of radioactive leftovers from around Europe.

Eventually, I arrived at the gates and found myself smiling endearingly at a small man with a large clipboard and a larger air of self-importance. When I told him I had a holiday home just down the road, he shook his head resignedly, asked me what I had in the back of the car, and nearly sucked his false teeth down his throat when I told him about my cargo. Had the cement not been set hard, he explained with grim satisfaction, it would not have been a problem. As it was, the contents of the bags had obviously become concrete, and must therefore officially be classed as grade 'B' building rubble, and not be allowed through the gate under any circumstances.

As I reversed out of the queue, the man gave a very false smile and called out that there was a free building rubble dump at Cherbourg, but that it was closed for the summer. I could always, he said, go to the mayor of my own village of Néhou and hand him the problem. Driving away to the sound of triumphant sniggering, I remembered that I have seen the weasel-faced man before, and that he comes from our rival village of St Jacques.

Had I expected my story to win any sympathy from Coco, I would have been disappointed. What I got was that very French expression of mixed incredulity, irritation and resignation which is usually reserved for vegetarians, pedestrians and Britons trying to speak French.

What I should have done, he explained as if to a child with learning difficulties, was to go straight to the town hall at St Sauveur with my problem. Having filled in the necessary forms, I would then have been granted an audience with the mayor - were he not away on a hunting trip in the Alsace region with his friend the mayor of Néhou. Had he been on duty, the mayor would have checked my forms, inspected my cargo, then signed a docket and revealed the secret location of the St Sauveur rubbish tip. The whole process would have taken no more than a couple of hours.

As I contemplated the next two weeks of carrying a quarter of a ton of concrete on my every journey around the peninsula, Coco looked at the sky and his empty glass for inspiration, sucked his teeth in the accepted manner, then said there was, perhaps, another solution. The local association of binmen was staging its weekly lunch at the Flaming Curtains at that moment, and some of them would have arrived in their official vehicles to save on private petrol costs. Were I to send them my compliments together with a good bottle of wine, Coco was sure they would turn a blind eye to certain items being loaded into the back of one of the dustcarts.

A little later, the bags had been transferred to Coco's purple Land Rover, and we had returned to the Bar Despond to enjoy a glass of strong cider, and to talk about the way big problems can be made to disappear with the application of a little common sense.

My mission for the day accomplished, I had time to drop in to enjoy an encounter with my favourite butcher. Although there is now a supermarket at St Sauveur, the town still boasts two bakeries and three butchery shops. The discount prices at the Super U are enticing, but buying bread and meat is a very serious business, and many townspeople still like to get these items from a specialist rather than a shelf. At the premises of Mr Rillette, they can also enjoy a spirited debate about the best way to prepare, cook and serve their purchases.

Our master butcher is justly proud of every steak, black pudding and cow's tongue he sells, and in the case of a new customer or a foreigner - and especially an Englishman like me - is naturally concerned about what will happen to his wares before they reach the table. While not actually refusing to serve me when I first arrived on the premises, he quite abruptly asked what I intended doing with the finely-cut slivers of pig's liver he was wrapping up like an expensive present. When I explained that they would be lightly brushed with oil, shown the grill, and then served on a bed of golden fried onions, he nodded almost approvingly, but was clearly outraged by my proposal of baked beans and chips as the side dish. After a lively exchange, we finally reached a compromise, and agreed upon gently simmered baby spinach leaves and sauté potatoes. Since then, it has become a mutually enjoyable tradition that any visit will always involve a discussion on what I intend to do with my purchase. Rather than become impatient at the delay, any other customers will be more than happy to join in the debate and come up with their proposals.

This afternoon, after finally agreeing on the preparation and cooking of my leg of local lamb, we had quite a severe disagreement over the origins of the beautifully crafted cottage pie on display in the window. When I said it was gratifying to see him offering traditional English dishes for his customers to try, he retorted that everyone with a morsel of knowledge about food knew that the great French *cuisinier* Parmentier invented the dish. When I stirred the pot by asking if Mr Rillette knew the difference between the British way of making cottage and shepherd's pie, he said that he would be surprised if the average English town dweller would be able to tell the difference between a thatched roof and a shepherd's crook, let alone beef and lamb.

Having left my master butcher to savour his victory, I was crossing the square when I saw a small and furtive figure slipping away from the bakery. Despite the large *baguette* obscuring his face, I easily recognised the diminutive form and characteristic gait of our elusive plumber. To his family and friends, he is known as Emile Souder. To his many British customers, he is known as Godot. Half the settlers in our area spend a good deal of their time waiting for Mr Souder's promised visit, and all fawn over him like overly obsequious courtiers at the palace of the Sun King. For to offend Mr Souder is to risk excommunication and, come winter, suffer the miseries of under-performing heating systems, burst pipes or even a blocked septic tank. It is not that Mr Souder is particularly skilled at his trade, but he is the only plumber in town, and those in other areas are always busy letting their own customers down.

As the town's sole practitioner in the mystic arts of moving water and human waste from one place to another, Mr

Souder has acquired the arrogance of a football star who every premier team in the country is eager to sign. Rather than a tradesman, he now sees himself as a celebrity and artist, and consequently likes to display his work rather than conceal it beneath floorboards or walls. Not for him the shortest and most discreet route between any two points when he is installing pipes. His installations are his signature, and nobody could mistake a radiator or shower put in place by Mr Souder. Sometimes, and especially after a good lunch, his work has an almost surreal appearance, and if he were a painter and not a plumber, he would definitely be a Dali rather than a Constable.

But regardless of my opinion of his design criteria and the astronomical level of his hourly rate, I have serious need of Mr Souder. It has been nearly two years since we regularly used the septic tank, which my friend René Ribet allegedly installed at La Puce, and the smell in our bathroom suggests that it needs an urgent service. It may be that it merely requires the traditional solution of a dead cat flushed down the toilet bowl to re-start the vital bacterial activity, but the mysteries and working of any *fosse septique* are far beyond my understanding. Besides, I would not know where to find a dead cat. But the need for action is pressing.

It is difficult for the average British town dweller to appreciate the importance of a satisfactory means of disposing of the contents of a toilet pan, but all over France, what is happening or not happening inside one's septic tank is a matter of almost daily discussion between British settlers, particularly over dinner.

Pursuing him to the steps of the nearby greengrocery store, I laid a hand on Mr Souder's shoulder, and he dropped his *baguette* in shock. As he turned and recognised me, a look of relief crossed his face as he saw that I was an anxious customer and not an outraged husband. Apart from seeing himself as an unparalleled virtuoso of the pipes, Emile Souder also likes to think of himself as something of a ladies' man. He does not have the commonly accepted looks and charm of a successful philanderer, even in France, but he is a man of some importance in the area, and works hard to maintain his reputation as a pistol of great note. In this field of activity at least, he is a realist, and concentrates on the plainer wives, who are not used to improper suggestions from men, and especially not from their husbands.

Apologising for the shock I have given him, I explained my problem with the septic tank, and after I had to endure my fifth bout of teeth-sucking that day, he promised to call round and look at it as soon as he was free. Confidence restored, he picked up his loaf, bade me goodbye, tweaked his small but intricately styled moustache, adjusted his boiler suit, and scurried up the steps into the grocery shop.

It is a safe bet that I shall be waiting for our Godot for weeks to come, and that, as he left, he also had other thoughts on his mind than the state of my septic tank. I know that the owner of the shop is away on the goodwill hunting trip to the Alsace, and that his wife is running the business on her own. She is of mature years and has a rather startling squint, but is generously proportioned and is said to be of an accommodating nature. Whatever the alleged reason for his visit, I fancy that our elusive and lecherous plumber was calling in for more than a bag of Brussels sprouts.

Animals, whom we have made our slaves, we do not like to consider our equal.

Charles Darwin, English natural historian (1809-82), from Notebook 'B' (1837-8).

FOUR

No rain for almost a month, so the story of what counts as a severe drought in this part of Normandy has made the front page of the regional newspaper. Old Pierrot has even appeared on Cherbourg Radio to recall the last time there was such an arid spell, which he said was the summer of '82. From the nature of his reaction, the interviewer obviously did not realise that our immortal was referring to the summer of 1782.

According to the official weather commentators, this year's combination of early floods of rain followed by a prolonged heat wave will result in a record crop yield. This is good news for farmers, and our vegetable plot and miniature vineyard. A long hot summer will also help produce a bumper harvest of tourists, which is good news for the whole region. Despite being in what many people would think of as the wealthy north, the Cotentin is officially rated as one of the poorest areas of France, and every centime of outside money is always welcome. A long hot summer will help everyone, whether they work on the land, or at relieving visitors of their holiday money. It will also make all the outdoor festivities much more enjoyable if the sun shines.

In the patchwork of small fields around La Puce, the cattle corn is approaching the height of a small elephant's eye, and everywhere there is a sense of anticipation as each town and village gears up for what is known locally as the season of fetes and forgetfulness. As the women say, the forgetfulness part means that most of the men will not remember to go to work the day after each of the events greeting and celebrating the summer. They, of course, do not appreciate what hard work it will be getting around all the fetes, fairs and festivals over the coming months, but as the men say stoically, marking the approach of the summer solstice is an ancient tradition which must be kept alive at all costs.

At the Mill of the Flea, the days grow ever longer, but speed by as we work to make good the depredations caused by our two-year absence. My wife has already mended and used the cement mixer to great effect, while I have been advising on the work to be done, attending Jolly Boys Club meetings, and doing other vital research for my new book.

Having fixed the leaking roof on the mill cottage, repainted the outside of the roadside farmhouse, mowed the water meadow, dug and seeded a huge vegetable garden and repaired all broken fences and gates, Donella has now turned her energies to further rebuilding and nurturing her menagerie. She spends hours every day with her animals, and sometimes it seems she prefers their company to mine. Like many apparently practical and sensible women, my wife seems to believe that most animals have much more sense and sensibility and much less savagery in their hearts than the majority of people, and especially men. It is not that she is some sort of rabid sentimentalist who puts other species before humans; she just finds animals refreshingly honest and open about what they want. As she says, if a dog is going to bite you, it usually makes its intentions quite clear beforehand, and doesn't lick your hand first. I don't know if this is strictly true, but, thinking about some of the people I have done business with over the years, I can see her point.

Taking my wife a cup of tea in the mill garden this morning, I found her apparently eating a large worm, while our two hens looked on with no more than casual interest. When I said I would be happy to cook her a proper breakfast, Donella explained she was just showing Gert and Daisy what other chickens like to do. What she doesn't accept is that, although the soil at La Puce is abundant with fat worms, lush and tasty grass and other free food that chickens are supposed to like eating, our hens are so well fed on laying mix, *cordon bleu* quality mash and expensive maize niblets that they cannot be bothered to scavenge for common and garden food. This has left them with lots of excess energy, which they now devote to finding new escape routes from my former shed and the surrounding compound I have built to keep them safe. Quite clearly, they have already realised they are in a particularly soft billet, and now see themselves more as guests at a hotel than working birds. Accordingly, they can become very tetchy if I do not provide the required room service and facilities at the right time.

The established routine is that I arrive promptly in the morning, let them out, collect the eggs and clean out the hut while they take a leisurely breakfast and consider options for their day's outing. On the first morning after their arrival, I wandered down just before noon to find the shed door hanging on one broken hinge and both birds clucking angrily by the feed store. When I arrived early the next day, I opened the now heavily-reinforced door and found them glaring at me from the roosting shelf as if I were a chambermaid who had surprised a pair of guests in bed.

Gert and Daisy are also becoming increasingly adventurous in exploring the far reaches of the ten mostly wild acres at La Puce, and I spend a good part of my time building ever higher and stronger fences around the mill garden. Donella is philosophical about their wanderlust, and says it is better for them to range free and enjoy their days exploring the terrain than to be cooped up in a relatively small area. Her reasoning is that, if they did not want to explore, they would not try to escape from what she refers to as my concentration camp. One day, she knows, they will run foul of an animal or even human predator, but they will have had a good life. Whatever I say, she will not agree that I am working in their best interests as well as trying to protect our investment and maintain a stream of fresh eggs.

To be honest, I also don't like to be outwitted by a pair of supercilious and self-willed hens. It is generally thought that chickens are stupid, but my wife believes they are smarter in many ways than a lot of people we know. Having watched them work out new escape routes from what Donella has nicknamed Stalag Luft 17, I believe she is right. While Gert and Daisy would probably do no better than the average human contestant on a television quiz show, they certainly have a high level of animal cunning.

It is, of course, convenient for people to think that the animals they eat have no conscious thoughts or aspirations, but anyone who has seen what farm animals will do to get their way knows that this is not true. Jacques Délabré once told me that people used to keep their farm animals in the house, and knew how clever they could be. Nowadays, the animals we eat are kept well away from the home and treated as if they do not even know what time of day it is.

As the sage of the Jolly Boys Club often says when yet another example of human stupidity or folly is discussed at our meetings, as a so-called higher species, we do not set much of an example to the animal kingdom. As René Ribet says, just because most of us like a juicy pork chop, it does not mean that pigs are at all pig-ignorant.

I may have misjudged the Birdwoman of Bricquebec. When we arrived in the water meadow this afternoon, we found the homing ducks sitting contentedly on the island in the middle of the big pond. Donella thinks the three khaki Campbells flew no further than the streamlet at the far end of the meadow and hid till they became more confident about their new surroundings. I think it more likely they realised they would have a far more luxurious life at La Puce than in their former quarters. Whatever the reason, they have already made themselves very much at home, and their return has changed the balance of power at the pond quite dramatically.

Though small, they display a marked degree of self-confidence, and at times, their behaviour reminds me more of lager louts than farm birds. I did not think it would be possible to like or dislike a breed of animal, but, were they human, I am sure I would not enjoy their company for a quiet drink in my local. Like some small Scottish people I have encountered in bars around the world, the Campbell clan obviously like a fight. And this family obviously does not need a few drinks below their belts to put them in the mood.

The trouble started when my wife decided to give Psycho and his gang their high tea, and threw a handful of pellets on to the pond. As usual, at least a hundred multi-coloured goldfish came shooting up from the depths to fight amongst themselves for the lion's share. While Gladys the nervous mallard retreated further into the shelter of the long grass on the far bank, the three Campbells looked at the mêlée for a moment, exchanged glances, then dived enthusiastically in to the fray. Unused to such an invasion of their territory, the fish were clearly outraged, and left off fighting amongst themselves to turn on the mutual enemy. Under attack from all sides, the ducks ignored the food pellets, formed a circle and set about the fish.

Though they fought bravely, even Psycho's ferocious tribe was no match for the flashing beaks of the Campbells, and the battle was short-lived. Within moments, the fish had retreated to metaphorically lick their wounds, leaving the ducks to swagger about the pond in search of another opportunity for a good punch-up. Luckily for them, our giant muskrat has still not made an appearance, and it will be interesting to see what happens if he returns to reclaim his position as top dog in and around the big pond.

After all the excitement of the afternoon, the day drew gently to a close as we settled down beside the caravan to enjoy the sunset, and talk about our plans for the future.

I agree with Donella that I must get on with writing the new book, but, as I said, that will take time, and we must take full advantage of any money-making opportunities that the summer may bring.

Over the years at La Puce, we have tried every sort of scheme to bring in some extra income; all have failed miserably, and some spectacularly so. This is not, I hope, because my ideas are unimaginative or impractical. In fact, my wife thinks my schemes have often been *too* imaginative. When we have the occasional falling-out over money, she accuses me of being a dreamer, and reminds me that we have always lost money as a result of my attempts to make a small fortune from what she calls hare-brained ideas. I usually remind her that history is full of examples of inventors and entrepreneurs and even visionaries who have been ahead of their time, and who had to face ridicule and failure before the rest of the world caught up with them and their innovative ideas.

I am convinced, for example, that my project for bottling and marketing the waters of our stream would have been a great success had they not been so badly polluted by chemicals and cattle droppings. Similarly, my idea of staging activity weekends for metal detecting clubs to locate the miller's secret hoard would have been a sure-fire winner if we had managed to get any bookings. My accidental invention of the garlic-flavoured car deodoriser should have been an instant success in France of all countries, but once again I was ahead of my time, and not a single company or bank had the vision to go into partnership with us and provide the necessary start-up capital.

Despite the setbacks, I know that the big idea is out there, waiting to be made real and at last bring us money, recognition and, most importantly, security for the future. But, while we are waiting for my books to become best sellers or the idea for a really lucrative project to arrive, I accept that we must look for a more certain way of making ends meet.

Like everyone who needs an income to make the dream of settling in France a reality, we have considered all sorts of ways of making a living by working from home. Unlike many would-be settlers, I have rejected the obvious ideas simply because they are so obvious that everyone is competing in the same market; or more usually because we could not afford the initial investment. Or sometimes because we know that the reality will not live up to the dream.

At least once a week I receive a letter from a reader who intends buying a ruin in France and converting it into *gîte* accommodation. As my correspondents invariably say, the simple beauty of their plan is that they will be doing for a living what they have previously paid to do for a holiday. Instead of just two weeks a year, they will be able to spend their every day in rural France, and their visitors will be actually paying for them to do so.

As I usually respond, there are several drawbacks to this proposal which should be considered before the plan is put into action. To begin with, doing for a living what you previously did for pleasure often loses its appeal when it becomes work, as many British *gîte* owners, most British publicans and probably all prostitutes would confirm.

Then there is the first and immutable law of French property development to take into account. This states that the true cost of turning a collection of ruined farm buildings into an attractive and functional accommodation centre will always be at least double what you worked out when doing your original guesstimate. Also, there will be lots of problems you did not think of when building your palace of dreams over dinner or in the local pub. More importantly, the final reckoning will usually be more than you can afford, especially if you have to add the interest on borrowed money to your regular overheads.

Quite apart from the second French property law (that the running and maintenance costs will always be much higher than you estimated), there are two other potential pitfalls.

The first is the likelihood that the behaviour and character of some of the people who will rent your accommodation will be marginally worse than a particularly ill-behaved raiding party of Goths and Vandals.

The second is that there are now apparently more people offering holiday accommodation in France than the number of visitors who actually stay here each year.

Having said all that, many people make a good living and a good life by putting up and putting up with paying visitors. But I know and accept that I do not have the temperament for what is undoubtedly a vocation. My experience over the past decade of having people and even former friends to stay at La Puce is that, not only am I invariably glad to see them go, but that they are even happier to be going.

Whilst we sat and talked about ways of surviving until my true worth as a writer is more widely acknowledged, a sudden wind came up and danced across the surface of the big pond, creating a myriad of ripples, swirls and ever-changing patterns. At the far end of the water meadow, a scurry of dark clouds passed across the tops of the line of oak trees marking the boundary of our land, then moved on to leave a limitless expanse of pure azure blue, dotted with tiny puffs of cotton wool far, far overhead. As if unwilling to leave such a perfect day behind, the sun lingered above the tree-line before slipping away to reveal a darkening sky suffused with a glorious, rich glow. Slowly, the canopy of orange and russet red turned to gentle velvet, and the first stars of the evening appeared.

While we sat in quiet pleasure and watched nature putting the greatest artists of history casually in their place, I heard a small splash and saw that Gladys had left her hiding place and ventured on to the pond. She swam hesitantly towards the island, then stopped as the Campbells became aware of her presence. As my wife reached for a stone, our new lodgers encircled the huge but timid mallard. For a moment they remained frozen in a moonlit tableau, then the largest of the three Campbells suddenly turned and swam unconcernedly away, followed by his gang. Gladys looked after them for a moment, then fell in line, and the small procession disappeared behind the island.

Clearly, nature had eventually triumphed over circumstance, and the Campbell family had accepted a new member. Smiling with pure delight, my wife put down the stone, and we settled back to enjoy the rest of the long summer evening.

For me, however, the magic of the moment was marred by nagging thoughts of our constant financial worries. I know people who say all they need is a roof above their heads and enough to eat to be happy, but they are invariably people with plenty of money which they never seem to spend. I must do something to ensure that all we have here is not threatened.

Donella is so in love with La Puce, it would break her heart if we were to lose our home. I think it would also break mine to let it happen.

Another day gone, and not a single word of the new book written. I have told Donella that I may have caught writer's block, but she says that as far as she knows, it is not a contagious disease, and besides, it only affects proper writers. All I have to do, she says, is keep a diary and dress it up a bit with my philosophical ramblings. Not being a creative writer, it is of course impossible for her to understand just how difficult it is to get down to work when there are so many distractions and jobs to do around La Puce, and especially if the muse is not to hand.

As any professional wordsmith will tell you, the hardest part of writing for some sort of a living is making a start each day. If the words do not flow immediately, I see no point in labouring on. When I am at the Bar Ghislaine or the Flaming Curtains in good company and with a glass in my hand, the ideas come unbidden in brilliant, lightning-like flashes of inspiration, and I have already amassed a huge collection of beer mats and cigarette packets covered with astute observations and witty lines. Apart from deciphering them the next morning, my problem is actually transferring those easily-won thoughts and ideas to proper sentences and paragraphs for the new book. People who write for no more than pleasure often tell me how lucky I am and what a wonderful job I have, but they do not know the torment of being a creative artist with a severe case of writer's block, a deadline to meet, and the season of fetes and forgetfulness on the horizon.

When it is at last written, the new book will be the fifth in what I had always intended to be a series of one. As my wife says, as long as people ask for more, I must keep on writing about our life here at the Mill of the Flea. But a dozen deadlines have arrived and flown, and now it is crucially important that I have the final draft ready for publication by autumn. According to Donella, all I need to do to finish the book on time is sit down at my desk and churn out the two thousand words a day that she has set as a reasonable quota. In truth, I have done no more than make a few outline notes on the computer since we arrived back at La Puce.

To begin with, I tried showing my wife draft pages from the manuscripts of previous books in the series and pretending they were that day's output, but she became suspicious and started reading them, so the game was up. Because of all that has happened in England, we have not published a book for nearly two years, and our financial situation is approaching red alert. Our French bank manager is a decent and normally tolerant man, but has already started calling to suggest that we make some severe economies. He said that he thought my offer of regular deposits of fresh eggs and vegetables in place of money was not much of a joke, and when I said we would be virtually self-sufficient come the autumn, he made his own attempt at a *plaisanterie* by saying he did not know I had been building a brewery at La Puce.

Last month, he called to welcome us and our overdraft back to Normandy, and said he had just received a sympathy card from our English bank manager. Donella says it is helpful to have a banker with a sense of humour, but she does not know that the jokes are wearing thin as our situation gets worse. Last week, he called to suggest we either sell the roadside cottage, or even the whole of La Puce. When he had assured me he was not joking, he said he had been reading the papers and was amazed at what English people would pay for property in Normandy, even somewhere like La Puce.

He also gave me the telephone number of an estate agent who is a friend of his, and suggested rather pointedly that I go and see him before too long.

Literary constipation still has me in its grip. After an hour of sitting dejectedly in the mill cottage this morning, the sound of our postman's moped buzzing away from the top of the track gave me the excuse to escape from another session of inactivity. I also hoped that the day's collection of postcards and letters might contain some ideas to kickstart my leaden brain.

Several hundred people write to the Mill of the Flea every year to tell us how good or bad they think my books are, and often about their plans for buying a home or living in France. Over the years, we have enlisted a small army of fellow settlers who regularly send us stories to prove that their lives in France are sometimes even more bizarre than ours. Their experiences often provide material for my books, and sometimes even I find them hard to believe.

Some years ago, a woman claiming to be an ardent francophile wrote to a French-themed magazine to say that I should be ashamed of myself for making such offensive and inaccurate comments about such a wonderful country and its people, and that I was obviously a little Englander who had no appreciation or understanding of French rural culture. In response, hundreds of readers with homes across the Channel wrote to ask if she had ever actually been to France, and that their villages and the people who lived in them were in some cases uncannily similar to those in our area. One correspondent said that, going by his own experiences with some of the people in his commune, I was probably watering down my stories to make them printable.

Along with the regular correspondence from all these Friends of the Flea, I receive the occasional manuscript from people who, like me, have written about their experiences of living in France. Some are information and advice books rather than memoirs, and today's post included a three hundred page manual devoted to the installation, care and maintenance of the septic tank. I did not have the time to read more than a few pages, but found it interesting and will write and suggest the author approaches a specialist publisher. I will also suggest he might care to make the narrative more gripping by including a few anecdotes along the lines of the dead cat technique.

As well as the inevitable bills, there was also an interesting letter from a new reader, who said he had recently bought an old country property in the Calvados department. The building is to be converted into *gîtes*, and though the project was going well, he said he had a delicate matter to broach. He and his partner are of the same sex, and they had been wondering how the local people would be likely to react to their relationship. He also mentioned that they are strict vegetarians.

I shall write back to say I am sure they will find little prejudice or concern amongst the locals with regard to their sexual orientation, but it might be as well to keep the vegetarianism a secret till they have settled in. In my experience, the French take a very relaxed view of most matters concerning sexuality, but can be prejudiced to the point of bigotry when it comes to people who don't eat meat.

Another letter had obviously been written in some haste, as the sender was about to drive from the Midlands to catch the first available ferry to France. He explained that rather than compete in the overcrowded holiday accommodation market, he and his wife had taken the unusual step of buying an old house which had been converted into apartments for renting to students at the University of Tours. The couple's overall game plan was that income from the apartments would just about cover the mortgage, then provide a reasonable pension when they retired to live in France. The building had come complete with tenants and a resident caretaker, who unfortunately spoke as little English as my correspondent speaks French. The caretaker, who seemed remarkably similar to our friend René Ribet, also appeared to have a great liking for the local *eau de vie*, which had made communications even more difficult during the purchase. All had, however, been going smoothly till the new owner arrived at his home in Birmingham after work to find a long and impenetrable message on the answerphone from his distant caretaker. After an hour of replaying the tape with a dictionary to hand, he had managed to pick out and translate what seemed to be four key words. Often repeated in varying degrees of excitement, they were 'drugs', 'dogs', 'bite' and 'police'.

At the time of writing and even after calling in a French friend and replaying the tape to destruction, our correspondent was unsure if the caretaker was trying to tell him that the tenants' dogs had bitten the police when they raided the house in search of illegal substances. Or that the police dogs had bitten the tenants and perhaps the caretaker as well. Or even, as his interpreter insisted that the obviously worse-for-wear *concierge* had actually said, that a gang of gendarmes had broken in to the house, and in their drug-crazed frenzy attacked and savaged a completely innocent dog.

The French are wiser than they seem.

Francis Bacon, English lawyer, philosopher and essayist
(1561-1626).

FIVE

Although there is still no sign of our giant muskrat or
the crayfish gang, the swallows at least have returned to La
Puce, so summer cannot be far away. I shall see if the clump of
pilewort by the river has bloomed and proved the countryside
lore that the two always arrive together.

It is a beautiful day, but my wife is not in a good mood.
This is because she knows I have not made any progress on
writing the new book, but also because my plan to surprise her
with a mate for Ermintrude had a distressing outcome.

Donella was very disappointed when we arrived at
market yesterday morning to find the goose season over.
Everyone who wanted a young bird to fatten for Christmas has
bought one, and the Bricquebec traders obviously make no
allowance for people who are mad enough to want to keep a
goose as a pet. But I had what I thought was a good idea.

Leaving my wife doing some hard bargaining for a new
pickaxe handle at the hardware stall, I sought out a trader who
runs a *foie gras* farm and has a thriving pitch at market. Coming
from a family which has lived in the same remote part of the

peninsula for generations, he speaks very broad patois, but seemed agreeable when I asked him if he would sell me one of his fully-grown geese as a surprise present for my wife. He was clearly bemused when I explained the bird must be of attractive colouring and appearance and definitely male. But as this special order would hike the price up considerably, he said he would be more than happy to do business with me.

According to plan, I told Donella that we were going on a mystery tour, and we arrived in mid-afternoon at the gate leading to the farm. As she does not approve of the traditional method of turning geese's livers into a highly-prized and expensive delicacy, I suggested she stay in the car while I found the farmer. Telling him all was ready for the big surprise, I asked my wife to shut her eyes and wait for a very special present. Right on cue to my signal, the man arrived at his gate, carrying a goose. As I had hoped, it was very large and imposing in appearance, snow white and for all I knew, male. Unfortunately, it was also dead.

As it was too late to stop my wife opening her eyes or to try and revive the goose with mouth-to-beak resuscitation, I paid the farmer and we drove back to La Puce in silence, with the corpse respectfully laid out in the back of our estate car.

I have tried to placate Donella by giving the dead goose a solemn funeral and burial in the mill garden, and have promised I will return to the farm tomorrow to buy a more lively bird. I will also stop off at the garden centre and pick up a range of plants and seeds as an extra present. Donella will be pleased, but there is another reason for my sudden interest in her vegetable plot.

Apart from home brewing, I have never been particularly inspired by the idea of self-sufficiency, but my wife has such green fingers I am beginning to think that my joke about paying the bank charges in fresh produce might not be such a bad idea. We may not be able to sell many of our vegetables to local people, but the barter system worked very successfully for thousands of years before money was invented. I shall have a word with the proprietors of all my local bars and see how they feel about setting up a system of exchange this autumn, with, perhaps, a cabbage being the agreed value of a glass of beer, and a string of onions worth a whole evening's drinking.

A shock this morning when we arrived to let the escape committee out and saw that Ermintrude was not in the grotto. We spent a frantic time wading along the river and calling for her before hearing a distant honk from the big pond. Arriving on the bank we saw her being hotly pursued around the island by the Campbell clan, led by the youngest male, who appears to be the ringleader when they launch an attack. Strangely, Gladys had joined in the chase, and from her attempts to mount our goose, she is either a lesbian, or we shall have to rename him Gladstone.

Ermintrude is the most amiable and gentle of creatures, and it made me very angry to see her being harried and sexually assaulted. I know one should not try and interfere with the sometimes brutal ways of nature, but I spent the best part of the afternoon harassing the Campbells from the leaky dinghy while Donella tried to coax Ermintrude out of the water. She is obviously lonely, but it is sad to see her trying to befriend a gang of bullies just for the sake of company.

Eventually and as dusk fell, we managed to get our lonely goose to follow us back to her safe home at the grotto, with Donella laying a trail of maize while I hid behind a tree and did my best to sound like a lovesick gander.

I have found a mate for Ermintrude, and I think Donella will be delighted. Telling her that I was going to town to see a man about a dog, I went straight to the *foie gras* farm and made clear to the owner that this time I wanted a live gander. After looking thoughtfully at the wad of money I was waving, he disappeared, then returned with his arms wrapped around what looked like a small actor in a pantomime swan suit.

The giant bird was brilliant white, with a long and very pointed beak, and looked more than capable of seeing off the entire Campbell gang with one wing tied behind its back. Despite my ingratiating smile, it began hissing violently as soon as the farmer tried to stuff it in to the car, and I made sure to keep out of range. Finally managing to tie its legs together and cram it through the tailgate, he stood back, took my money, and advised me to buy a large metal dustbin on the way home. When I asked why I should need a dustbin, he smiled wryly and said I might find the lid useful as a shield when the goose attacked me. Some ganders can be exceptionally aggressive, he said, but in all his years as a *foie gras* farmer, he had never seen a male take such an obvious and instant dislike to anyone.

I drove away with the car rocking from side to side as my reluctant passenger tried to get over the back seat and at me, and in the wing mirror I could see the farmer shaking his head in what could have been sorrow at losing such a fine specimen, or sympathy for me. Though I thought he might be having a joke at my expense, I decided to stop off at the hardware store in Bricquebec and buy the biggest and strongest metal dustbin in stock.

We have introduced Big Albie to Ermintrude, the pond and the Campbell gang, and the initial outcome was not what we had hoped.

Rather than stamping his authority immediately on the ducks or making advances to Ermintrude, the giant gander came charging out of the back of the car and made straight at me. Luckily, I had the dustbin lid to hand, and was able to deflect the worst of his attack, though my best shirt will no longer be fit to wear in company. When he had tired of denting my shield, Albie waddled truculently down into the water and swam off to sulk behind the island, completely ignoring his intended partner. Unlike most bullies, the Campbells are obviously not cowards, and the two males and Gladstone followed him for what was clearly going to be a serious confrontation. As the air was filled with a series of belligerent honks and quacks, Ermintrude let out an outraged squawk and went to the rescue.

By the time I had grabbed the dustbin lid and launched the skiff, the fracas was over, and the Campbells had retreated to neutral territory. Ermintrude then did a victory lap around the pond, with Big Albie meekly in tow. The more I see of animal behaviour, the more I realise that, though it is obviously a mistake to try and make direct comparisons between the human race and other species, relationships between the genders can be strikingly similar.

Bad news on two fronts today. I have made no progress beyond thinking up a possible title for the new book, and Donella has seen through my latest ruse of copying passages from other travel writers' books and claiming them as my own. She is now threatening to lock me in the roadside house and away from the distractions around the mill cottage until I pass the day's quota of pages under the door.

We have also had a catastrophe with our commercial wine-making project. For once my wife's green fingers have let us down, and our miniature vineyard has died. We called in a professional viticulturist for his verdict, and when he got over the shock of learning we were trying to make wine - and particularly red wine - in Normandy, he told us that all the vines were diseased and would have to be burned. He didn't say as much, but I could see he thought the infestation was a judgement visited on us by the wine gods for daring to grow black grapes north of the Loire Valley. This disaster has ruined my plans to produce a limited edition of *Vin de la Puce* as a novelty item for sale to British tourists at Bricquebec market.

If things continue to go wrong with my money-making schemes, I shall have to think seriously about our bank managers proposal that we sell off parts or even all of La Puce.

To console myself for the loss of our vineyard, I have been on a pub crawl. My excuse was to test out reactions to my idea of swapping our home-grown vegetables for drinks this autumn. No takers so far, but I only visited a dozen bars today, and there are many more establishments in the region which may see the advantages of having me as a regular customer as well as a supplier.

A welcome diversion this afternoon when a caller arrived in a cowboy hat and some distress. As Donella was busy sowing enough courgette seeds to see us and our barter customers through the winter, I turned the computer off and invited our visitor into the cottage to tell me her troubles.

A strikingly attractive and obviously refined lady who once worked as a Jerry Hall lookalike, Felicity said she had recently moved over to live in a hamlet not far from La Puce. Originally from Hampstead, she is not familiar with rural Norman plumbing systems, and had received a nasty shock that morning when her flushing toilet refused to do its duty. Exploring the garden, she had seen a large manhole cover, and managing to prise the lid off with her parasol, found herself looking at what seemed to be several years' worth of apparently petrified excrement.

Promising I would either take a look myself or call in a local specialist, I asked her how she was settling in, and she said that, apart from the encounter with the septic tank, she was enjoying her new and very different life in the French countryside. In the past week she had received a proposal of marriage from a complete stranger, been invited to her carpenter's home to taste his home-brew *calva* and inspect his bandsaw, and only this morning been chased around her sofa by a neighbour who had promised to empty the solidified *fosse septique* with a hammer and chisel.

Overall and apart from the problems with the drainage, she said, the social life and activities here seemed not very different from Hampstead, and life in the Norman countryside promised to be anything but boring.

Friday the thirteenth, and my computer has broken down. When I told Donella, she said that four is considered the unluckiest of numbers in Japan, and elsewhere in the world it is seven, so she will not believe that it is the date and not me that has caused the problem.

Although I now have a genuine reason for not working on the manuscript for the new book, I am seriously concerned that I will miss the much-revised publication date, and more income for the year will be lost. Although they are hardly in the blockbuster league, the initial sales of each new book provide a vital boost to our yearly royalties, and it will be disastrous if we miss the Christmas market. While Donella looked through the telephone directory for a specialist who can resuscitate the writing machine, I went down to the big pond to think about our situation, and the rotten hands in the game of life that the fates have dealt us recently.

Thanks to my improvidence, we have no pension, and with the years speeding by at an ever-increasing rate, I am often full of fear for the future. When I was young, I was sure that it would not be long before my talents would be recognised and rewarded, and if I did not succeed as a writer, there was always the chance of a massive win on the football pools. With retirement as far away as the next millennium, I felt sorry for people who were going to spend their working lives in an unexciting career, with nothing at the end but a sense of unfulfilment and a pension. Now those people are looking forward to a comfortable and secure retirement, I can see the attractions of having had a proper job.

We have always lived a precarious existence when trying to survive on my writing skills alone, and in the early days of our marriage I drifted through what seemed an unending series of mindless jobs to top up our income. The invariable routine was that I would take a new job to escape the tedium of the last, then become bored with that one as soon as I had mastered the basic skills required.

For more than a month, I worked at a factory which made cardboard boxes to hold blocks of ice cream, and it nearly drove me mad. People who talk about the dignity of honest labour have obviously not tried factory work.

Each night, I would walk through the gates, clock on and go to my bench. Waiting for me would be a wooden palette loaded with twenty thousand squares of perforated grey cardboard, a ruler, and a hammer. My job was to measure out an inch's worth of the cardboard squares, place the stack on the desk, then knock the perforated edges off with the hammer. I would then put the finished sheets on an empty palette, and repeat the process.

For the next eight hours I would continue the ritual, wondering all the while why fate had decided I should be born, loved and nurtured by my parents, avoid all fatal accidents while growing to manhood, then end up helping to make homes for blocks of vanilla fudge ice cream.

Amongst the workforce, there would always be a number of students, working during their holidays to earn some tax-free income to see them through the coming term. From their point of view, they were also finding out what it was like to work for a living, and at future dinner parties would be able to tell their friends that they knew what manual work was all about. The difference between them and us was their knowledge that they would be going back to college or university after their stint in the factory. For us, there was no promise of escape.

The cardboard box factory was a non-union workplace, wages were low, and to reach what was called the bonus rate and earn a little extra, I had to knock the corners off exactly 4,800 sheets of cardboard an hour. The worst part of the job was dealing with the very last stack of sheets on the palette, then hearing the creak of a trolley as the next giant load was dragged alongside the bench.

To try and keep sane and give me something upon which to focus, I became obsessed with beating my quota and the arrival of the next trolleyload, and would attack the mountain of cardboard sheets in a frenzy the moment it reached my bench. As a result and much to the displeasure of the other men on the line, I began regularly exceeding the hourly rate, and sometimes earned almost as much in bonus as in wages. One day, I earned more than the shift foreman, and knew my days were numbered.

After I left, I heard from a former workmate that, because I had proved it could be done, the company had upped the hourly quota.

Sometimes when I am feeling particularly depressed, I think of my time in that factory, and that some of my former friends may still be there, attacking their two hundred millionth ice cream carton and waiting for the final knocking-off buzzer to set them free.

Leaving the big pond and walking back to the mill cottage, I decided that, even though it was after dark, I would unlock the chicken house and give Gert and Daisy a bonus hour of freedom while I kept watch for Mr Fox. Remembering what it was like during my days of captivity in the cardboard box factory, it was the least I could do.

The start of what promises to be another scorching day, and I have been on early shift at the big pond. My computer is still broken, so Donella thinks my time will be best spent in trying to protect the goldfish from the Campbells, and at the same time acting as a matchmaker between Ermintrude and her reluctant mate. I have tried singing snatches from romantic arias to encourage them to get to know each other better, but Big Albie still seems more interested in attacking me than wooing Ermintrude. He obviously does not have the sexual drive of the Campbell males, who are all unashamed rapists. When I bought them from the Birdwoman of Bricquebec, I assumed they were a family, but they are certainly not acting like any respectable family I know, unless they have picked up their incestuous habits from what is said to go on in the remoter reaches of the Cotentin marshlands.

At least once a day, the two male Campbells will gang up on the lone female, and take it in turns to climb on her back, force her head beneath the water and have their way with her. It is a short and most brutal affair, and I now see what psychologists mean when they say that rape is about power and not just sexual gratification. Occasionally, the larger of the two Campbells will also mete out the same sort of treatment to the younger drake, and unless he is bi-sexual, I think he is trying to show that he is still the dominant male.

As if that were not enough, Gladstone is now beginning to join in the assaults on the female Campbell, and Donella is concerned for her safety. Apart from a bald patch on the back of her neck, Hen seems little affected, takes the daily attacks in her stride, and afterwards goes through a thorough cleaning and preening ritual before unconcernedly rejoining the males. She is a tough little bird, and is already proving herself more adventurous than the male members of her dysfunctional family.

My wife has said we must buy at least one more female duck to take the strain off the beleaguered Hen, but I have been toying with the idea of buying and booby-trapping one of the decoy ducks on sale in the gunsmith's at St Sauveur. With a small hole drilled in its wooden rear and some ground glass glued in the appropriate place, I might just be able to give the rapists a painful lesson.

Donella has vetoed my plans for the booby-trapped decoy duck on the grounds of common humanity, and we now have another female duck at the big pond. Blanche is, as her name suggests, as pure white as Big Albie, and has a fetching pink bill and sparkling eyes of Ava Gardner green. She is very plump and shapely, and, were I a permanently randy drake, I think I would find her very engaging.

The problem is that she is a duck who thinks she is a goose. The trader at the mobile market at Bricquebec said that, though she is big for her breed, she is very young, and as we discovered, she is obviously missing her mother. When we let her out of the carrying box, she waddled straight over to where Ermintrude was grazing and tried to put her head under our amiable goose's wing. Now she follows her foster mother and father everywhere, and they have become very protective of her. As soon as they saw Blanche, the Campbell males made their salacious intentions clear, but were sent packing by a furious joint attack from Ermintrude and Albie. The result of all this is that we now have another unnatural family on the big pond, and poor Hen is still under daily assault.

At least one positive aspect of the situation is that Big Albie has stopped attacking me on sight and concentrated his venom on the Campbells, so I am free to move around La Puce without my dented dustbin lid permanently at the ready.

Although the geese are standing up to the Campbell clan, Donella is worried about Psycho and his gang.

We have seen no signs of the giant muskrat that lived in and around the big pond for several years, and though I used to resent his destructive presence, I am beginning to miss him and the sense of natural order he established. Over the years, he ate every expensive plant we put in the pond, doubled the household bread bill with his voracious appetite for specially imported English sliced bread, and turned the bank into a minefield of ankle-turning escape trenches and tunnels. On one occasion, he even bit me when I was trying to re-thatch the roof of his lair. But he inevitably became a member of our extended family, and I used to enjoy watching him going about his business and keeping all the other denizens of the pond under control.

I suspect he thought of me as just another inferior species, especially when he appeared on the island and settled down to engage me in staring-out contests, which he invariably won. Now he has either moved on, died of natural causes or been shot by hunters, and I think even the goldfish are missing him as they become an endangered species. We can no longer throw food pellets on the water, as the ducks have learned to hide behind the island and wait for the fish to come to the surface. The Campbells now see the pellets as bait rather than food, and have become expert fishermen. Whatever naturalists might say, our ducks have definitely developed a taste for fish.

Donella is already talking about transferring Psycho and his diminishing tribe to the safety of the grotto, but I do not think we should give the Campbells the victory. One of the Jolly Boys Club members is a keen coarse angler, and I shall ask him about the chances of catching a suitably large and aggressive species of fish and installing it in the big pond. I think an encounter with a giant pike might give the Campbells almost as great a shock as my booby-trapped decoy duck.

No visitors, telephone calls or post today, and I am

beginning to think that our computer expert is related to Mr Souder, the elusive plumber. With Donella busy in her vegetable garden and all relatively quiet at the big pond, I was at least able to sneak away and attend this week's Jolly Boys' media study committee meeting. It is at these gatherings that we take it in turns to report on national events and stories that we think best reflect our country's culture and attitudes to life and living.

Many Britons might think that rural French people would not have the slightest interest in the goings-on in other lands, and particularly Great Britain. As a race, our nearest Continental neighbours may appear insular, and certainly none of my French friends could list more than a handful of departments in their own country, let alone have a stab at naming, apart from London, any major cities in Britain. Some would have a problem recognising the name of a town more than twenty miles away from their own village. Nevertheless, they enjoy hearing stories about other European countries, and particularly Britain, which confirm their prejudices and make them feel superior as the only nation in the world which conducts it affairs with such a unique blend of passion, pragmatism and logic.

The first item of home news selected by the committee concerned a recent incident in the south of France, when local people fell out with a religious cult that had set up shop in the foothills above their town. Their immortal leader having caught a cold and died suddenly, the members decided to erect a hundred-foot-high concrete effigy of the great man. Objecting to being overlooked by the monstrosity, the townspeople secured an order that the statue be demolished. When the cult members lodged an appeal against the order, the local police force simply moved in and dynamited the statue while awaiting the decision of the court. Discussing the report, all the committee members agreed that this was a fair and equitable outcome to the situation.

The second story concerned a pet shop owner in Nancy,

who went to the expense and trouble of putting up a neon sign outside his premises announcing that his wife was having an affair with the local banker. After hearing all the evidence, the judge fined the wronged husband the equivalent of £5000 for infringing the banker's privacy. Opinion among our committee was divided on the fairness of the judgement. Some members thought the decision just, while others said the cuckolder should have been ordered to pay the pet shop owner a respectable sum for not only promoting his virility, but also advertising his bank.

Next, it was my turn to come up with a story reflecting life in modern-day Britain, and of particular bemusement to my fellow members was a full page article in the arts section of the *Observer*, reviewing a recent stage presentation of something called *The Vagina Monologues*.

According to the article, the show is a ninety-minute distillation of the thoughts of more than 200 women about their most private part, and involves the narrator posing questions along the lines of: 'If your vagina was getting dressed, what would it wear?' Printed in the programme for the show, I told my stunned audience, is a recipe for vagina salad, which includes bean sprouts representing female pubic hairs.

After a moment's silence as the elderly members of our debating society digested the information and doubtless considered the likelihood of their wives serving up a crispy vagina salad for lunch, I explained that, according to the report, the monologue has been well-received in more than twenty countries around the world, despite the difficulties of accurate translation.

Following a further reflective silence, Jacques Délabré pointed out the irony that the feminists behind the production would probably be outraged to learn that 'vagina' actually comes from the Latin for 'sword-sheath'. On the subject of the difficulties of presenting the monologue in so many different countries, our resident philosopher shrugged, then remarked that translation should not have been much of a problem, as after all, a *con* is a *con* in any language.

The wise man respects Nature, and gardeners are the guardians of Nature.

French version of an ancient Chinese saying.

SIX

The days seem endless, and the water meadow is aflame with the hues of early summer.

Nourished by the combination of intermittent rain and the prolonged heat wave, our ancient hedgerows are heavy with colourful blooms and blossoms, and we shall take full advantage of nature's bounty when autumn arrives.

But in the midst of this verdant display of fecundity, we have had a harsh reminder of the realities of country living. Big Albie has either done a runner or been abducted. Donella is inconsolable, as she is not only distraught at the thought of what might have happened to our giant gander, but blames herself for his disappearance.

Last night, after seeing that all was well at the big pond, she forgot to close the gate leading to the mill garden, and is convinced that Albie must have somehow wandered up the track on to the main road, and is now alone, lost and frightened somewhere in the vast stretch of marshlands beyond. She has set off to search for him with a bag of his favourite cracked maize in her pocket and unrealistic hope in her heart, but I think she must know she is on a wild goose chase.

Clutching at the weakest of straws, she asked me to stay at home in case a passing motorist may have picked Albie up and is calling round the local farms to ask if they have lost a gander. I have said I will stay close to the telephone, but I think even she accepts that this is hardly a likely scenario, and that any local motorist seeing a plump goose at the roadside would be more likely to aim his car at it rather than stop to ask if it was lost and needed a lift.

Apart from all the trouble and expense of finding a mate for Ermintrude, I too am sad to have lost our new family member. I have tried to comfort my wife with the thought that, as happened with the Campbell clan, his absence may only be temporary. But unless a minor miracle occurs, I think it a safe bet that we have seen the last of Big Albie.

After a long and predictably fruitless search of the *marais*, Donella has returned alone, and I have made matters worse by inventing a story to comfort her. While she had a bath, I said I had forgotten to mention I had seen a local farmer driving up the mill track early this morning. I added that I was sure that Donella had, in fact, shut the gate leading to the big pond last night, and that Mr Trefle had probably been poking around in our absence and left it open. Although untrue, the story was credible, as we often catch our nosey neighbour prowling around on our land. He lives almost a mile from La Puce, has no right of way through our terrain and does not farm any of the surrounding fields, but seems obsessed with what we are doing with our land. We also suspect he is not above helping himself to any small items that he thinks we will not miss.

Unfortunately, I completely underestimated Donella's reaction to my story. Rather than taking the opportunity to relieve herself of guilt for having left the gate open, my wife now believes Mr Trefle has taken Albie, and has demanded that we drive to his farm so she can confront him. Normally, Donella will go to considerable extremes to avoid unpleasantness with other people, but not when it comes to animal welfare, and especially the welfare of one of her own animals.

We are back from our visit to Mr Trefle's farm, and no damage has been done to Anglo-Norman or neighbourly relations.

When we arrived at the bottom of the lane leading to his yard, my wife let out a triumphant cry as she saw a large white goose pecking at a clump of grass by the gate. Luckily, before she could try to positively identify it as Big Albie, at least another dozen identical birds came honking up to the gate.

After I had managed to persuade her that our goose was probably not amongst them, she agreed reluctantly that we should take the matter no further. And as I pointed out, as well as the collection of ganders, there were also a number of grey Toulouse geese in the yard, all of whom were very similar in appearance to our own Ermintrude. Even if Big Albie has found his way to Mr Trefle's farm, a sort of natural justice may have been enacted. We will have lost a fine gander to our neighbour, but we quite possibly gained Ermintrude from the same source. If she insisted on an identity parade to see if Big Albie had moved to Mr Trefle's farm, we would in all fairness have to tell him about our own gift from heaven. Whether or not he was missing a goose, he would certainly lay claim to Ermintrude, and we would then be bound by moral duty to hand her back.

For once, my wife agreed with my reasoning, and we drove back to La Puce in reflective silence. Even having known Big Albie for such a brief time, it is hard to lose him and not know how he would have settled in. But on balance, I think it better that my wife believes he may be alive and well at Mr Trefle's farm, rather than on a plate on a complete stranger's table.

Following an uncomfortable telephone conversation this morning, I have taken my bank manager's advice and been to see his friend the estate agent about the possibility of selling La Puce. Although I feel guilty at keeping the situation from her, I have not told Donella that we may have to leave our home of twelve years and settle for somewhere smaller and more economical to run. With luck it will not have to happen, but I know the agent will tell our bank manager about my visit, and this may stave off any unpleasantness over the state of our account. Hopefully, I will also be able to come up with a money-making scheme before the new book is out and the royalties begin to trickle in.

The estate agent is based at Port Rabine, a former fishing village which has become a trendy yachting haven. It is in a very exclusive area, and prices for property overlooking the sea are almost as high as they would be in some parts of Britain. They are especially high when a house has been owned by and sold on to another Briton.

Although I find the village a little twee for my taste, it is undeniably attractive. There is a 14th-century church on the foreshore, and the small market square is ringed with shops and rugged stone cottages once occupied by poor fishermen who would not have believed the prices their homes are now fetching. Adding to the appeal to wealthy second-home owners, the less attractive parts of the town with its modern buildings, council houses and supermarket are safely hidden away inland. Naturally, the estate agent's office is located within a stone's throw of the sea, and it is rare to visit Port Rabine without seeing at least one English couple looking in his window and dreaming their dreams.

After persuading his haughty secretary that Mr Sourcil had actually granted me an audience, I was escorted in to meet a small, dapper man, with very carefully manicured fingernails and a distinct air of self-satisfaction. He was wearing obviously expensive and fashionable clothes of quite startling hues, and was a fine example of the French professional class's penchant for dressing like British TV game show hosts.

Having dispensed with the polite preliminaries while he sized up the condition and quality of my home-made Bermuda shorts and the shirt which Big Albie had savaged, I explained that my wife and I were thinking of selling our large country property, and he smiled. When I explained that our home was not on the coast but half an old mill cottage and a small farmhouse on the main road to St Sauveur, the smile disappeared, and he looked fleetingly at the door as if thinking about calling on his secretary to see me off the premises.

He looked even more depressed when I explained that the two properties at La Puce had been restored and converted to our style and taste, and that we had done most of the work ourselves. After examining his fingernails carefully, he explained that there was little call for houses in our area from his sort of clientele, but that he would call by at some time in the future to look La Puce over and have some photographs taken for his files.

I thanked him for his interest, told him that I had already taken a wide selection of appealing photographs, and gave him a folder which included a rather clever panorama showing the full extent of the overgrown fields, fallen trees and jungle-like water meadow. As he flicked through the pictures, I noticed that his eyebrows rose and fell regularly like small boats on a swelling sea. While he put the folder in the bottom drawer of his desk, I asked him for a rough estimate of the value of our home, and he looked, if possible, even more uncomfortable. After more facial gymnastics and an attack on his highly polished teeth with a gold fountain pen, he said it would not be possible to value such an unusual property from the photographic evidence alone, and promised to visit us the following week and inspect the premises personally.

Outside, I watched through the window as Mr Sourcil emerged from his office to share a joke with his secretary, then I turned and almost collided with a rather unusual couple. As the woman shuddered and backed away from me, I noticed they were both wearing clothes of exactly the same pastel shade of orange. He was tall, stooped and had a faintly apologetic air, while she was tiny and bird-like, with hair and makeup so carefully arranged that she looked like a Japanese doll.

After apologising for frightening them, I learned they were English, and in search of a holiday home in the area. As an idea began to form, I tried to warn them of the ridiculous prices of the houses within sight of the sea, but the woman shrugged dismissively before putting on a pair of sunglasses and explaining that they had recently sold their eight bedroomed designer- restored farmhouse (with large heated swimming pool) in the better part of Provence, and had just been discussing how reasonable the prices in Port Rabine seemed to be. Their only problem, she added, would be to find something of the size and quality to which they were accustomed. They had already seen one large property overlooking the sea that she quite liked, but had discovered that it was the town hall, and not for sale. Another house was quite promising, but, as the woman explained with a delicate shudder, the tiles on the roof were completely the wrong colour.

Carefully structuring my sales pitch, I explained that I have lived in the area for more than a decade, and might be able to give them some help and advice with finding a property which would exactly match their requirements. In fact, I said, I knew of a most distinguished and well appointed property in the heart of the peninsula, with two fully and painstakingly restored buildings, a river, several ponds, a water meadow and a copse. Though not award-winning architect designed, the cottages were in very good nick, and the roof tiles of a very suitable colour for the overall ambience and style of the buildings. The property had, I said, only just come on the market, and the owner (a celebrated intellectual and author) was asking what might at first seem a high price because of the social cachet that the property commanded. Perhaps it would be too expensive for them, but I would be happy to act as an intermediary and save them the agent's fees if they thought they might be interested.

Having baited the hook, I suggested we take coffee at the bar over the road, and excused myself so that I could return to Mr Sourcil's office, reclaim the folder of photographs of La Puce, and remove the shot of the mismatching roof tiles that René Ribet found in a skip and used to repair the damage of the Great Storm of 1998.

In the Café Rodin, I found the man looking at a menu while his wife fingered the table cloth with the same sort of expression as Mr Sourcil wore when he looked at my photographs of La Puce. Deciding to drop any continuing attempts at subterfuge, I confessed that I was the actual owner of the country property, and handed them the folder. After looking at only one photograph, the woman turned noticeably pale and made off to the toilet, leaving her husband to apologise and explain. His wife, he said, suffered from a condition which was so rare that the medical profession had had to make up a special name for it. The cause of her problem was that she had read so many interior design magazines that she had developed an allergy to any mix of shades or hues which did not conform to the strict rules of current fashion. The condition could cause his wife to have a panic attack at the mere sight of a pair of curtains which she thought did not match the colour of the wallpaper alongside them. In extreme cases, she could be physically sick. He did not say so, but it was obvious that the photograph of our living room had sent his wife running for the toilet. I sympathised with him, put the folder away and decided it would be pointless to continue my sales pitch. If a snapshot of the interior décor of our home was enough to give his wife a bout of nausea, an actual visit to La Puce could well prove fatal.

While we waited for her return, I learned that he was as passionate about entomology as she was about colour harmony, and told him about my wife's problem with insect attacks. He then said that the mosquito was his particular speciality, and that there are more than 2500 species, with the most common and bloodthirsty being the *culex pipiens*. Within two days of birth, the female of the species is ready to mate, and the male of the species will have up to eight partners in its short lifetime. Providing, that is, that their genitals have not been torn off in the frenzy of copulation. The midge may be known as the curse of Scotland, but is to be found in vast numbers wherever the conditions are suitable. From my description of La Puce, it sounded as if we were providing a perfect breeding ground.

When I asked him if there was any guaranteed repellent, he said that, if there was, he had not heard of it. After all the modern chemical preparations had failed to do the job properly, the top scientists in the field were currently working on a solution made of extracts taken from various common plants, and whoever came up with a really effective protection would be sure to make millions. He had himself experimented with all sorts of compounds, but his particular speciality was discovering and developing new ways of dealing with and disposing of flying pests rather than repelling them. His research in the field began when they had been troubled with mosquitoes at their home in Provence. His wife had objected to the traditional swatting method, as the smears left behind rarely matched the colour of her rag-rolled walls. After much trial and error, he had come up with a solution as effective as it was simple. Using a hand-held car vacuum cleaner, he would creep up on the resting mosquitoes and hoover them up for later disposal.

After this small success, he had moved on to greater challenges. Hearing that a neighbour was plagued with a colony of hornets so large and savage that even the local fire brigade refused to take them on, he had used a much more powerful domestic vacuum cleaner and applied the same basic technique. Placing the tube over the entry hole to the hornet's nest when he was sure they were at home, he had put the machine on turbo drive, sucked out the entire colony and then set fire to the bag. The method was a hundred percent effective, but in case I should want to try it out, he should warn me of an almost fatal oversight made by a friend who tried the same technique.

Unfortunately, the man had not realised that a key selling feature of his wife's new machine was that it had no bag. When he had opened the machine, the naturally unhappy hornets had emerged to take revenge. The victim had survived the encounter, but the locals still talk about the lottery that took place in the local bar, with the jackpot going to the entrant who guessed nearest to the number of stings he had suffered during the attack.

Home from my mission to Port Rabine, I trundle down the mill track to find a battered old van with English number plates parked in the turning circle. There is no sign of the driver, but the back of the vehicle is filled to the brim with a sofa and two armchairs, at least four young children of assorted colour and gender, a very large and excitable dog and an even larger motor cycle with a skull and crossbones on the petrol tank. Obviously, we are being visited by a fairly typical buyer of my books.

In the summer months, we can expect to receive several calls a week from readers who drive down the track to see if we are at home, and often to discover if we and La Puce actually exist. By and large they are not what many people would call normal. One elderly lady recently wrote to me to say that I obviously inspire extreme reactions to my work, and that she believes I am becoming a cult. At least, I think she meant cult, as her writing was rather shaky.

On most occasions, I enjoy these unexpected visits from our readers, providing they have not called to complain about something I have written or ask for their money back. Invariably, I learn something about human nature from these encounters, and often I am rewarded with personal stories that I could not have hoped to invent.

Inside the mill cottage I meet Kevin, a tall, beleathered and spectacularly tattooed young man who calls himself a mostly reformed biker. Although he looks like he would still enjoy the traditional Hell's Angels pastime of biting the heads off live chickens, he seems a highly intelligent and pleasant young man. With him is his partner, a young black woman called Serena, who is an aromatherapist and holistic massage specialist.

Until recently the couple lived in a former council house in Watford, and had sold it for three times what they had paid for it a few years previously. Having a reasonable sum of money for the first time in their lives, they decided to make a new life across the Channel, where they would be able to buy the sort of interesting and isolated property which would have been no more than a hopeless dream anywhere in Britain. Since last week, they have been the owners of what is left of an abandoned fort on a tiny island in the gulf of Quiberon, in Brittany. There are no water, electricity or other services on the island, but Kevin has already drawn up plans to use the ancient motorbike as a generator, and is even thinking about building a desalination plant to get free water from the sea. He has also packed a broken jet-ski in the back of the van, and when it is mended, he and his partner will be able to commute to and from any work he can find on the mainland. In the meantime, Serena will be building up her portfolio of people in the area who can be persuaded that regular exposure to aromatherapy will enrich their lives. I do not tell them that I have often written about the naivety of people who think they can become mobile hairdressers, marketing consultants and (especially) aromatherapists in rural France, and in this case, I think the young couple may well make a go of their plans.

One thing I have learned from meeting so many different people with so many different schemes for successfully settling in France is that there are no rules. In the past ten years, I have met people who seem to have had all the mental, physical and financial qualifications for making a go of their plans, and yet have gone home with their dreams in ruins. I have also met those who seem to have had even less of a chance of survival across the Channel than us, yet have won through. In any case, and as Kevin says, he and his partner have nothing to lose except the money they never expected to have anyway, and just scraping by on their very own island must be better than living on a former council estate in Watford.

Before they leave to start their great adventure, Kevin tells me of an embarrassing encounter when leaving the ferryport at Cherbourg. As the overladen van rattled up to the customs post, the officer on duty had obviously heard the children talking in the back and asked for details of their cargo. Wanting to impress the official with what he thought was his reasonable French, Kevin said he and his partner were moving over to settle in France, and, together with the couple's assorted children and his vintage motor bike and broken jet-ski, they were carrying some old and very battered furniture. This brought immediate interest from the officer, who summoned his colleagues to inspect the contents of the van. When they had seen the three piece suite and stopped laughing, the officer had explained in perfect English that rather than *mobilier* as in furniture, Kevin had said *immobilier*, and had, with other minor but important distortions of the French language, claimed that inside his van were a number of old and very distressed English estate agents.

This morning I was cornered in the mill garden by a coalition of the Campbell family, Gladstone the mallard, Ermintrude the grey goose and Gert and Daisy the hens. It was a tense few moments, and they refused to allow me to go even after I had given them a double handful of maize each. When my wife arrived to see what all the fuss was about and had shooed them away, I explained I had been singing a Puccini aria while working on the chicken-wire fence alongside the feed store, and that the birds had obviously recognised my voice and sought me out. Having got over the surprise of our encounter, I said I was quite pleased that I would now be able to communicate with our livestock and perhaps even get them to obey simple commands.

Donella merely laughed and said that the music-loving Ermintrude had probably led them to complain about my mangling of *Nessun Dorma*, but that given my new ability to be able to talk to the animals and my lack of progress on the new book, she would now call me Dr Doolittle.

We have been to Bricquebec to see the grand final of the European Football Cup. As usual, England was knocked out very early in the competition, which must have brought a sigh of relief from policemen and bar staff in the continental cities which were to host the qualifying stages.

After their side's totally unexpected victory in the World Cup, there has been an upsurge of interest in football in France, and particularly so in our area, as the national team's coach was born in Bricquebec. The match against Italy was shown on a giant screen in the town hall, and the atmosphere and behaviour of the spectators was predictably distinctive.

For at least two hours before kick-off, it seemed every family in the town came through the doors, all laden down with enough equipment and provisions to see them safely through the event. Rather than whistles and hooters, of course, they had brought sizeable hampers of food and drink, and one group struggled through the door with a full-size gas stove and set of tables and chairs so they could have a proper dinner while joining in the fun.

Eventually, and despite a number of official complaints from people who had not finished eating, the match started, and the Norman version of cup fever took hold. When Italy played well and threatened the French goal there was ungrudging applause, and when the French side scored there was a small and almost apologetic cheer. But in the closing moments the tension and excitement finally had its way, and when France scored the winning goal and the whistle blew to signal the end of the match, the hall erupted.

While we joined in the scrum of hugging, kissing and whooping, I saw an elderly farmer watching me with a somehow poignant smile as I cavorted around the hall with a girl who said she was his daughter. Later at the bar, I apologised for my abandoned behaviour, especially as I was not French. He looked at me for a moment, then said that tonight, everyone in the hall was French, and he knew that, even though I was a foreigner, most people in the area seemed pleased that we had chosen to live with them. He also said that the moment reminded him of an evening many years ago, when the news of the Liberation of France had come. There was no comparison, of course, in the significance of the two events, but it was good to see such happiness and pride in being French again.

We left the celebrations in the early hours, after spending some time trapped in a cavalcade of cars circling the town with horns blaring as if a hundred French wedding processions were taking place. It was clear that there would not be much peace in Bricquebec that night, but as my wife said, it was very unlikely that there would be a single broken window or pool of vomit to be found come the morning.

Dawn is breaking beyond the giant cedar tree in our orchard, France is the soccer champion of all Europe, and I have been sitting at the big pond, thinking about the meaning of life, the nature of success, the part fate plays in our progress from birth to grave, and the mysterious disappearance of fruit-flavoured Spangles.

Over the years I have debated the subject of success and its relationship to happiness with hundreds of people. Some have been poor, some bitter, and some very wealthy, but none have been able to give the answers I seek. Some people say winning the game of life is all a matter of luck, but I have observed that it is invariably those who claim to be the most unlucky of people who say this. Others say that being able to see over the hill to what the future holds and having the nerve to take great risks is the true path to success.

Whether where we end up is the result of luck, fate, self-determination or a mixture of all three forces is a subject that has been puzzling philosophers since man has had the ability to reason, so there is no particular reason that I should ever be able to solve it. The nearest to a conclusion I have managed to reach is that life seems rather like a game of cards. You are given a constantly changing selection of hands, and it is how you play them that will determine the outcome. This theory conveniently includes fate and self-determination, and gives me a good excuse for blaming any problems on being dealt a rotten hand.

Whatever the true answer to this particular mystery of life, I am sure of one thing. However sorry I feel for myself from time to time, billions of people around the world would rather be in my shoes. That is something I always try to remind myself of when in the depths of self-pity, and especially when I start to believe that, when our ship of fortune finally docks, I will be waiting at the railway station.

I have just returned from a JBC meeting where the main item on the agenda was the election of a committee devoted to promoting the active participation of sport in the village. As the president said, the committee's main objective will be to discover, train and groom a local sporting star of tomorrow. The only sporting activity I have ever seen our members indulge in is the occasional game of indoor *pétanque* to save them straying too far from the bar, so I found this sudden enthusiasm puzzling until I recalled France's recent success on the football field. Now that they are champions of the world and Europe, every Frenchman has naturally become an instant and lifelong expert on every sporting activity as well as fashion, food, wine and love-making.

Inevitably, there is more to the scheme than an altruistic desire to put the village on the map and help a talented sports person to reach his or her potential. The Néhou Search for A Sporting Star committee has already drawn up a draft contract which will ensure that they will receive a substantial majority of any future earnings of their discovery in perpetuity.

What I have found particularly irritating about this instant national interest and expertise in all sporting matters is that the French are now claiming to have invented cricket. According to today's *Presse de la Manche*, some ancient documents which have suddenly and conveniently been unearthed prove that the game was brought over from Northern France and Flanders in the 14th century by soldiers, and adopted by their British counterparts. According to the article, even the word 'cricket' comes from Norman patois for 'chasing with a curved stick'. During our debate on the matter, I argued that it seemed strange that there should be a particular expression for such an activity, but Old Pierrot pointed out that there is a patois expression for every activity and pastime known to man, even those which have not been invented yet. He went on to claim that he had actually played in an impromptu cricket match against a scratch team of English archers during a lull in the fighting at the Battle of

93

Agincourt. The other side may have won the battle, he conceded, but the French won the chasing-with-a-curved-stick game.

When I protested that England was the home of cricket, the president of the new sports committee pointed out that, for a nation that claims to have invented the game, we are not too good at it. To the casual observer who did not understand the rules of the game, the objective of our regular home Test matches against Australia would appear to be to force the visitors to take the Ashes home with them.

Why bother to tell the truth, when with a little effort you can make it entertaining?

WC Fields.

SEVEN

The weather has broken, and last night the rain gods returned from their holidays to remind us where we live.

Summer rain is far from unusual in Normandy, but it has been a uniquely dry spell, and as I lay snugly in the mill cottage bedroom early this morning, I found the staccato drumming on the tiles comforting. I read somewhere that WC Fields liked the sound, and that his wife played a hose pipe on their roof as a last gesture of kindness as he lay dying in his bed. Perhaps I will ask Donella to do the same for me when my time comes. She has already talked about burying me beneath the vegetable garden if I go before her, and says that apart from saving on the cost of a proper funeral, with all the beer I drink I will make a very effective fertiliser.

As I got out of bed, someone was becoming very excited in a particularly French way on the radio, and the *Marseillaise* was played at least twice in the time it took me to reach the bathroom. Then I remembered it was the eve of Bastille Day, so Normandy will be more shut than ever this weekend. This evening we shall be visiting the Flaming Curtains for the weekly meeting of the English settlers club, but before that I have an appointment with an overflowing septic tank. Donella can hardly object to me escaping from the book I am not writing, as the computer is still dead, and I will tell her that I will be doing some valuable research. With Mr Souder our official plumber still at large, it has taken me a little while to help our new friends to book an appearance of a very special specialist in the arts and crafts of waste disposal. But the appointment has been made, and this morning I shall be at the home of the Jerry Hall lookalike lady to watch him perform. If anyone can solve her problem with the solid sea of human excrement, it will be the region's undisputed *champion de la merde.*

I have arrived at the home of the lady with the obstinate septic tank. Felicity lives with her partner Jon in a pretty cottage in an isolated hamlet which has become known locally as Little England. It is said that British owners now outnumber French residents, but as there are only a dozen houses in the hamlet, I do not think this is a significant statistic.

In the ten years we have been living in this part of Normandy, the number of Britons setting up a permanent home here has steadily grown, and their arrival has been generally welcomed. Unlike in Wales, where English people buying country properties pushed the prices up to a level that young, local people could not afford, the arrival of foreign buyers here is not a cause of friction, as the settlers bring much-needed money and work to the area. Some also bring a life style and patterns of behaviour which give the local people an endless source of enjoyable gossip. Over the years, I have noticed that, like Cornwall, our part of Normandy seems to attract very individualistic and often quite unusual incomers. With property prices and rents a fraction of what they would be just across the Channel, expatriate Britons can live very cheaply in the Cotentin. When necessary, they can also go to earth quickly and most effectively.

Arriving beside the immaculately tended front garden, I narrowly miss driving into a huge hole, from which Jon emerges. I notice he is wearing a handkerchief tied round his nose and mouth, and as I get out of the car I realise why. His partner waves weakly from the kitchen window, and I see that she has abandoned her extravagant stetson hat, but is wearing what looks like a World War II gas mask. Having seen what his hand is covered in and thinking better of shaking it, I join Jon on a guided tour of the pit, and learn he has already prepared the ground for what may be a challenging task, even for Mr Pagaille.

What lies at the bottom of the hole is unlike any other sewage disposal system I have seen in all my years in the Cotentin. Rather than being perturbed by living on an underground lake of human ordure, Jon realises that he has uncovered something really special, and is as excited as an amateur Egyptologist who has just found the other half of the Rosetta stone in his back garden. While we inspect the exposed parts of what is clearly a substantial network of pipes, chambers and cylinders, he launches into a detailed account of how he approached the excavation.

As I have said before, an apparent obsession with the workings of waste disposal systems may appear strange and even unhealthy to the average town-dweller, but dealing efficiently with the contents of a toilet pan can assume crucial importance to those who live beyond a main sewage system. Most British buyers who find no disposal facilities existing in their new home opt for a septic tank, which will chemically treat and then dispose of the resultant sludge. Sometimes, they choose a cess pit, which is basically an underground room, the unadulterated contents of which are hoovered up by a specialist like Mr Pagaille when necessary, and then taken away for disposal or - it is said - to sell to a local farmer who wants some particularly rich fertilizer for his crops. Ruder devices may consist of a pipe running a short distance from the house and ending in a hole filled with brick rubble. At Felicity and Jon's new home, whoever paid for the installation of this maze of underground piping certainly got their money's worth.

Pointing out particularly interesting features of the installation as he takes me on a guided tour, Jon explains that, having seen a number of archaeological documentaries on television and wishing to follow the correct procedure, he began the excavation with a large shovel, then progressed to a garden trowel as he came to the more delicate stages of the operation. Now, he is using one of Felicity's silver-plated apostle teaspoons so as not to do any damage before Mr Pagaille arrives.

At his invitation, I lower myself down the side of the huge cylinder and land on a manhole cover which apparently leads to the main storage area. It may be my imagination, but the cover seems to be vibrating, possibly because of the pressure building up inside. I investigate, and see that in the middle of the metal disc is a small hole from which a thick slurry is bubbling. As I give the cover an experimental kick, the vibrating beneath my feet increases, the smell becomes ever more ripe, and a loud belch issues from deep inside. I exchange glances with Jon as the rate of discharge from the small hole increases significantly, and we both scramble out of the hole.

As we retreat to a safe distance, the sound of a labouring engine tells us that professional help is on the way. Preceded by a stench even stronger than that coming from the pit, an ancient tractor pulling a huge cylinder on wheels splutters around a bend in the lane. As it pulls up alongside the hole, I see that the rig is driven not by Mr Pagaille, but his assistant Eric. Almost as well-known in the area as his employer, Eric is remarkable for his attachment to his official overalls, and the large space that appears round him in any bar he enters, even on a busy market day. It is rumoured that the patron of the *Café de Paris* in Bricquebec once paid Eric the Lonely to become a regular at a rival bar which had been taken over by an ambitious newcomer. The story goes that the owner put his business on the market after only a month.

Trapped between the stench from the clogged septic tank and Eric and his equipment, we move upwind and await the appearance of Mr Pagaille. The news of Eric's arrival has obviously reached the other residents, and a small knot of spectators is already gathering on the edge of the pit. Most of them are from the hamlet, but some from quite far-distant villages. Mr Pagaille is known throughout the Cotentin for the style and dash of his performances, and always draws a crowd. He is held in particular awe as he not only cures his customers' problems, but is said to be able to analyse the standard of a family's cooking and dietary regime just by inspecting the contents of their sewage tank.

Clearly oblivious to the deep rumblings and the rank odour issuing from the pit, Eric the Lonely lowers himself into the depths and makes an initial appraisal. After a few moments, he climbs out again and stands looking down into the hole, scratching his head in what seems to be a mixture of perplexity and admiration. He then gives a long, low whistle, shakes Jon's hand, and explains that he has been working with Mr Pagaille for eight years, and has never seen a sewage disposal system remotely like this one. It is possibly unique. It may be the only device of its type in the Cotentin, perhaps Normandy, and perhaps even the whole of France.

At this news and in spite of the ever-worsening smell, there is an audible intake of breath from the spectators, and an almost visible swelling of local chests at such a singular claim to fame. A little boy darts off with his dog to spread the good news, and soon it seems the entire community has gathered around the hole. One anxious English woman suggests we should call the fire brigade and let them deal with what may be a dangerous device, but she is immediately put right by her Norman neighbours. The *pompiers* may be experts in their own field, and inimitable when dealing with floods, fire and rescue operations, and hornets and wasps' nests. But for such a challenge, Mr Pagaille is unquestionably the only man for the job.

As if on cue, the great man's arrival is signalled by the roar of a large engine, and I look up to see if he is to arrive in his own personal helicopter.

Disappointingly, a large flatbed lorry appears around the bend, and on the back is Mr Pagaille, standing in an almost heroic pose on the top of a large coil of piping. There is no actual applause, but a general shuffling of feet and appreciative murmurs as he climbs down and approaches the crowd, which parts respectfully to let him through.

Though large in presence, Mr Pagaille is a diminutive man, clad in a pair of well-tailored and crisp blue overalls with his name emblazoned on the back after the manner of a celebrated football player. The most striking aspect of his appearance is how kempt and obviously fastidious he is. His wellington boots look brand new, and his long, sensitive fingers appear as immaculately manicured as those of the estate agent at Port Rabine. This is clearly a man who does not intend to sully his hands with the manual side of his business. He is to be the *directeur* and not the actor in this drama.

Probably to show that, despite his celebrity, he has not lost the common touch, Mr Pagaille pauses to pat the nearest dog and tousle the hair of several children before beckoning his assistant to join him at a point some distance from the crowd. As the apprentice makes his report, accompanied by much arm-waving and pointing at the hole, Mr Pagaille nods gravely, asks a few questions, then raises an imperious hand as if to demonstrate to the spectators as well as his assistant that he has heard enough. He then walks slowly to the edge of the hole and stands with one hand on his chin, looking speculatively down at the grumbling collection of pipes and cylinders, dials and hatches. After taking a deep breath in the style of a wine taster testing the bouquet of a challenging vintage, he snaps back his head, reaches for the breast pocket of his overalls, and produces a pair of obviously new surgical gloves. With practiced ease, he pulls them on, and climbs down into the hole as his assistant urges the spectators to move back to a safe distance.

Mr Pagaille is out of sight for at least five minutes, and an air of unease descends upon the crowd. Surely, he has not met his match? Has he been overcome by the fumes? Worst of all, will the hamlet become known throughout the region as the site of the great man's first failure?

As troubled looks are exchanged and the shoulder-shrugging rate increases to an almost manic intensity, Mr Pagaille finally reappears, climbs slowly up out of the hole, and stands pensively looking down at the ground as he removes his gloves. While we watch and wait, he taps one finger against the bridge of his nose, then nods reflectively before taking three carefully measured paces from the edge of the hole and pointing silently down at an area of undisturbed lawn. His assistant nods, hurries to the lorry and returns with a spade. Following a brief consultation, Eric the Lonely begins to dig. Within moments, his spade has hit an obstruction. He lays down the spade, gets to his knees, and begins pulling up the remaining clods of earth by hand. Eventually, he stands up and steps back. His employer looks into the small hole, then regards the crowd as if checking they are paying attention. Then he reaches down, and with the flourish of a master chef revealing a particularly artful creation, lifts a rusty metal plate and beckons his audience to join him.

If the smell had been bad before, it now seems to have an almost physical presence, and one of the dogs lets out a howl and retreats down the lane with its tail between its legs. But agog to see what has been unearthed, we press forward and look down into the hole.

'*Merde*', breathes the man alongside me, and his description is demonstrably accurate. The manhole cover that Jon had discovered was obviously nothing but a red herring. It was not, as we amateurs had assumed, the major access hatch. By finding and unearthing the main entrance to this subterranean cathedral, Mr Pagaille has demonstrated precisely why he so richly deserves his reputation. As he says, Jon was understandably deluded into thinking that the manhole cover was the key to entry. But he is not the only one to have made this mistake. For many years, previous owners of the cottage had obviously been attempting to empty the cylinder by means of the small breather hole in the cover. They had believed that they were disposing of all the waste product, when they were merely scratching, as it were, at the surface. To be a true *spécialiste* in his field, Mr Pagaille concludes somewhat immodestly, it is necessary to have the mind of a great detective. One has to think oneself into the mind of the original creator, to understand how his mind, and thus his invention, worked.

With the aid of Jon's torch, I am privileged to be the third person in perhaps fifty years to look into the bowels of the vast device. It appears to contain generations of excrement, compressed into an almost solid mass. If giants still walked the earth, their bowel motions would surely look and smell like what lies before and below us.

An hour later, and the mammoth septic tank has yielded up its contents, but not without some energetic and hands-on work with a pickaxe and shovel by Eric the Lonely. The suction pipes have done their work, and the hundredweights of prime and well-rotted manure are about to begin their journey to some hopefully far distant field.

We pose for the official photographs which will almost certainly appear in the local paper, and Mr Pagaille is invited back to a neighbour's house for coffee and, I suspect, a free consultation as to the condition and quality of the owner's own waste disposal system and its contents. I stand and watch as Eric trundles off toward the town pursued by a dense cloud of flies, and think what a tale he will have to tell in his local bar this evening. It is just a pity, I reflect, that there will be nobody within hearing distance to learn of his historic encounter.

Having showered twice and mostly removed the evidence of my afternoon with Mr Pagaille, I am allowed into the car to attend the weekly meeting of British settlers at the Flaming Curtains.

Though there is no official organisation for expatriates in the area, a number of us have naturally gravitated to Coco's bar, and the result is our very informal association. The original purpose of the weekly gatherings was to improve our French, but most members have already accepted it is a hopeless cause. I read recently that a French linguist claims there are more than three thousand words that the French and English have in common. I have also heard it said that to get by in any foreign country it is enough to know five hundred words of the host language. If these two claims are true, millions of English people should be able to speak almost fluent French. Anyone who has seen the look of dread on the face of the average Briton about to ask for a cheese sandwich in a French bar will know that this is not so.

Arriving in the car park alongside the Flaming Curtains, I swerve to avoid running over a man with two crutches, a neck brace and one arm in plaster. As I drive slowly past, he lifts a stick in automatic and polite greeting, and promptly falls over. Albert *l'acrobate* is out for his morning stroll, and for once is not hoping to be run over. His nickname in the town is not an unkind joke based on his perennial injuries, but rather a compliment on his agility in achieving them.

Incapacity benefit in France is very generous, and, as in Britain, some people here make a living by persuading their doctors that they are unfit for physical work. The local doctor is not an indulgent man, so some years ago, Albert resorted to creating real injuries to ensure he would not be forced to seek gainful employment. He became quite adept at finding cracks in the pavement or walking through glass doors, but by last month he was running out of ideas for encounters and injuries to keep his name on the unfit-for-work register.

After a long session with a drinking crony in the Flaming Curtains, a plot was hatched which he thought would prove infallible. On the following day, Albert would step from the pavement of the high street just as his friend pulled out of the car park beside Coco's bar. Much practiced at impressive falls, Albert would throw himself dramatically over the bonnet, then be able to claim a severe back problem which even the sceptical doctor would not be able to refute.

The next day, all appeared to be going to plan when Albert walked briskly into the road as a black Renault approached. Unfortunately for Albert, it was not his friend's car, but an identical model driven by a visitor. To make matters much worse, the visitor was a Parisian taxi-driver. Obviously seeing no reason to stop because a pedestrian had been foolish enough to step in to the road, the driver kept going, and Albert's journey through the air was completely genuine. But far from being unhappy about the incident and resulting injuries, he is now a happy man. Not only will his genuine incapacities keep him safe from the threat of a job for years to come, he is also suing the Parisian for an allegedly huge sum, and has generously promised to share the proceeds with his fellow conspirator.

Having successfully avoided Albert, I have to swerve again as a wildly bearded man wearing long black robes and roller skates comes hurtling around the east wing of the church alongside the bar, executes a perfect flying hurdle leap over Morton the pub dog, and continues his circuit.

In the bar, I learn that Coco has installed his first guest

at the New Algonquin. The skater currently on his tenth lap around the church is a Scottish barrister who has left his wife to start a new life in France. He has told Coco that he was being driven mad by the falseness of his world and the huge sums of money he had to charge his rich clients, and intends setting up a practice in St Sauveur where he will be dealing with real people in a real world, and be able to help them in their times of need for a token fee. While helping the oppressed masses, he is also going to write a contemporary novel about Life. I admire his intentions and sentiments, but wonder if he will find his sort of reality here. In the Scottish way of sons of the gentry being given surnames as their first names, the new settler is called Cameron. He has moved in to a room above the Curtains so he can be near the heart of the town, and also, as Coco has already observed, very near to the bar at all times. There has even been some talk of installing a dumb waiter, so that he will be able to summon and receive liquid refreshments without leaving his work station.

As I order our drinks, I notice a man in a trilby hat setting up a huge array of amplification equipment in the corner of the bar. I look at Coco, and he shrugs like a prisoner who has accepted that he will shortly be mounting the scaffold. The fact that the intensely soulful looking man is assembling such a vast collection of loudspeakers is bad news. That he is wearing a trilby hat and has a wispy beard is much more serious. He is obviously a folk singer.

As an enthusiastic patron of the arts, Coco regularly allows amateur musicians to use his bar to showcase their talents, and finds it hard to refuse anyone, no matter how bad they are. Sometimes, the performers at the Flaming Curtains sing and play in tune. Occasionally and when they stick to covering the handful of tuneful and enduring songs the French have come up with in the past century, they can be quite entertaining. But our guest artist this evening is clearly intent on making us miserable with his own compositions about how hopeless life can be. As he begins to test his microphone by rehearsing the lyrics of a catchy little number about a country maid committing suicide in a Paris bordello after hearing that her lover has been killed during the Battle of the Somme and learning that she has contracted a terminal social disease, I grab our drinks and escape to the terrace.

Already assembled round the huge table is a fairly representative selection of the members of our expatriate community who regularly use the Flaming Curtains. I nod at a nice elderly couple who live outside St Sauveur, and who seem, when compared with the rest of our group, somehow oddly normal. Alongside them is a retired thespian, much given to flowing scarves and theatrical gestures. Anton claims to have had, quite literally, a hand in hundreds of top Hollywood movies and British television advertisements. He says he made a very good living standing in for close-up shots of the hands of such stars as Robert de Niro and Warren Beatty, acted as a stunt action double for Sean Connery's digits in several James Bond movies, and was the original walking fingers for the famous telephone directory television commercial. I do not know if what he says is true, but he certainly has beautifully cared-for and expressive hands, and takes great care not to overuse them, especially when it comes to putting one in the air to call for another round of drinks.

Anton is deep in conversation with a defrocked priest from Idlesworth, and next to them is Jean-Claude Goulot, who lives in the depths of the forest of St Sauveur, and is known locally more for his production of fine apple brandy than his abilities as a master carpenter. While not as famously elusive as Godot the plumber, Jean-Claude demonstrates many of the traits of the typical rural French journeyman, especially when it comes to getting a job started.

Just under five years ago, I asked him to give me an estimate for installing a pair of french windows in a convenient hole in the ruined end of the mill. He arrived on time, then spent an hour enthusing on the possibilities the ruined building offered someone of his skills and artistic sensibilities. At a very low cost and yet using ancient, seasoned oak, he could not only fit the windows, but also construct and install a huge water wheel which would be completely traditional, even down to giving a satisfying creak as it turned. Having made any number of intricate sketches and taken dozens of millimetre-accurate measurements, he then insisted I accompany him back to his workshop to select the lengths of prime wood for the job, and devise a precise itinerary for the operation. Two hours later, I found myself staggering the three miles home clutching a small sample of oak and a gallon of raspberry-flavoured *calva*. I see Jean-Claude at Coco's bar almost every day, and he visits us at La Puce at least once a week, but the hole still gapes in the ruined end of the mill, and the creaking mill wheel exists only in our imaginations. This, as anyone who has tried to restore a rural French property will tell you, is very much par for the *cours*.

It may seem unusual that one of the students at our weekly French lesson is in fact French, but Jean-Claude speaks in such a broad patois that he believes it a good move to re-educate himself in his own language so as to be able to communicate better with potential customers who live outside the area. Although it seems to me this could only have the effect of increasing the number of people for whom he is not going to do any work, that at least is his official excuse for being a member of our drinking and social club.

Taking my place at table, I see that another elusive tradesman is with us, but he is British, and at least has very sound reasons for avoiding any property restoration work. Bob The Builder is a winsome fellow who appears at irregular intervals with his yardstick and clipboard, allegedly in the process of providing estimates for restoration and improvement work for local English owners. When we first met, I asked him for some advice on a leak in the roof of the mill cottage, and it was obvious that he knew absolutely nothing about construction work. After a couple of drinks, he confessed that he was not really a general builder, but visits Normandy at least twice a week to stock up on low-duty tobacco, wine and beer for his many customers in southern England. As he told me, he found smuggling to be much more profitable and interesting than his former career as a policeman, so established his fictitious construction company and had his van signwritten in case customs officers on either side of the Channel became suspicious of his constant crossings. He says he has had the same length of roofing felt and bag of cement in the back of his van for more than four years, and so far nobody has asked for any more proof of his activities than his estimates for customers and properties which do not exist.

Before we have a chance to start asking each other the way to the nearest railway station, the folk singer begins the sixth renditioning of his personal tribute to Jacques Brel, and the bar empties. We then decide to give up all thoughts of an evening spent grappling with the intricacies of conversational French, pile into Coco's ancient Land Rover, and roar off in convoy to a Bastille firework display at the nearby castle. Also on display this evening is the mostly admirable French attitude to standard Health and Safety regulations, but there are no serious injuries when several stray rockets, a World War II thunderflash and a giant catherine wheel land in the crowd.

Taken together with Mr Pagaille's tour de force in the afternoon, and despite the best intentions of the folk singer, it has been a very enjoyable end to an intriguing day. Pleasantly tired and only slightly scorched, we have returned to the Flaming Curtains for a nightcap, and to try and sort our individual and mutual bar bills while contemplating into the small hours what a rich and varied life we are privileged to lead in our quiet and uneventful corner of Normandy.

No man but a blockhead ever wrote, except for money.

Samuel Johnson, English poet, critic and lexicographer.

EIGHT

The rain gods are busy elsewhere in Normandy, and never have I seen a sky so clear. This morning I laid on my back by the big pond and watched a tiny silver dart inching across the heavens, its vapour trail the only stain on a canvas of perfect blue. I just wish that our financial horizons were so cloudless.

Despite the dry spell, the recent combination of heavy downpours and soaring temperatures has brought about a humidity level which would make a rain forest mosquito feel at home, and for a week or more, Donella has rarely ventured from the house without her stocking mask. In desperation, she tried out the car vacuum cleaner method, but found it not at all effective in the open air. Her experiments also caused more gossip in the village when the driver of a passing tractor saw my wife running around the top fields in pursuit of a cloud of midges while wearing one half of an old pair of tights on her head, and wildly brandishing her new TidyVac Mk II Hand-Held Dustbuster.

Even though the air is much clearer today, Donella has decided to stay indoors with all the windows shut and a selection of insect repellent sprays and ointments to hand, while I have been sent to weed the vegetable garden and start work on yet another pond. Since the disappearance of Big Albie the gander, the sexual assaults on Hen and the bullying of Ermintrude and Blanche by the Campbell clan has reached new levels, so my wife has decided to take drastic action and segregate the males from the females. I have built and furnished a new luxury home by the grotto, and together with the new pond, Donella is hoping to create a safe refuge for our battered birds.

I claim to resent the extra work, but it has given me a good excuse to escape from worrying about my lack of progress on the new book and our mounting money problems. Although I pretend otherwise, I am also concerned for the well being of our female birds, and relish the opportunity for some heavy manual work on the land. I like the smell of the soil and feeling the sun on my back as the sweat runs freely, and then enjoying a long soak in the bath at the end of a productive day. When I was paid to wield a spade I found no reward in it, but when I dig my own land I feel a sense of achievement, and am at peace, and even at one with La Puce. It seems to me that there is a dignity in labour, but only if one does it out of choice rather than necessity. Another advantage of these occasional bursts of energy is that the hard physical work also gives me an excuse to eat and drink even more than usual.

Although Donella is staying indoors I shall have some help with the project, as Cameron the reluctant barrister and writer-in-residence at Coco's bar has offered to lend a hand. When we met at the Flaming Curtains and I told him my plans for another pond at la Puce, he said he would also relish the chance to get his hands dirty with some honest toil. He added that he is descended from a clan of sturdy Highlanders who worked the land and lived in simple crofts, so he is sure their skills with a spade are in his blood and soul. I do not know how much help he will be, but I shall take an interest in finding out how good a memory his allegedly working-class genes possess.

The new pond is finished, but no thanks are due to the mad lawyer of St Sauveur. He arrived an hour late and said that he had lost a wheel from his rollerblades just after setting out on the journey, and had to return to the Flaming Curtains to borrow Coco's mountain bike. When it had refused at the first serious hill, he had been forced to resort to a taxi.

After eventually finding a pair of wellington boots to his liking, I gave him a spade and showed him which way up to hold it, but he took no more than a couple of tentative prods at the turf before collapsing with what he said was a recurring back injury. He spent the rest of the afternoon sitting on the bank, drinking my beer and smoking my cigarettes while telling me what to do, and all the while extolling the virtues and rewards of honest toil.

When he had finished off a whole case of Heineken, he said that he had not enjoyed himself so much for a long time, then called a taxi to take him to the Curtains for a relaxing bath and another attack on his novel. Before he left, he pointed out that I had made one bank higher than the other, that the pond was far too small, and promised to come back tomorrow to show me how to do the job properly. Given my past encounters with the legal profession, I suppose I should be relieved that he did not charge me a consultative fee for his advice.

I have had an idea for a project which could, if successful, solve our current financial crises.

Sitting by the new pond and going through my daily routine of trying to think how we can make some extra money out of the land at La Puce, I noticed how well the various fruits of our hedgerows are coming on. Although we always have an abundance of hazel nuts, sloe, elder and blackberries, the hardness of the previous winter and combination of sun and rain through any growing year will determine which trees will prosper most. This year, virtually the entire length of the hedge between the water meadow and top fields is a pure virginal white, so there should be a huge crop of elderberries. Over the years we have tried all sorts of ways to make the best use of the tart black berries, including elderberry pie and even ice cream, but the fruit of the elder is an acquired taste. Each autumn, we donate our blackthorn sloe berry harvest to add flavour to Jean-Claude's yearly batch of home-brew Calvados, and receive two bottles in exchange. Last year yielded a particularly poor crop, so I mixed some elderberries in with the sloes without telling him, and when I called in for my bottles, he said he had to throw the whole batch away as it tasted foul, and would ruin his reputation as well as his palate if he kept it.

Now, I think I can see a way of making money from our miles of hedgerows. When our miniature vineyard died, I was stuck with hundreds of empty bottles and the equipment for making and marketing a special novelty batch of *Vin de la Puce*. Although the rest of Europe seems to think that only the pressings of the grape can make drinkable wine, we have a great tradition in Britain for creating alcoholic drinks from other fruits, and even vegetables. Looking at the virtually unbroken line of delicate white blossoms lining the water meadow, I do not see a beautiful but useless growth. Rather I see hundreds of bottles of Elderflower Champagne of the Flea.

Before returning to the mill cottage to share my thoughts with Donella, I remember my other important chore for the day, and stop off to weed the vegetable patch. Fetching the hoe from the garden shed, I see that the alternating heavy rain and strong sunshine has also worked wonders on what will be a vital contributor to my financial plan for the year. All our vegetables seem to be thriving, and some of the courgettes are already the size of small cucumbers.

Unfortunately, the weeds have also flourished. It is obviously going to be a particularly good year for ferns, and they are already threatening to take over the entire acre of garden stretching down from the roadside farmhouse to the mill stream. I find them quite attractive, and would be happy to leave them there, but my wife says they must go. I begin my work, taking care to remember the old adage that a weed is merely a plant you do not want. During my first weeding session on Donella's recently seeded vegetable patch, I pulled up what I thought was a host of baby ferns and showed them to her as evidence of my hard work. She was not pleased with my contribution, and said that rather than sprouting ferns, the hundreds of feathery shoots I had pulled up were virtually all the first, delicate growths of her carrot crop for the whole year.

We have run out of excuses for avoiding a confrontation with our bank manager, and been summoned to explain my 'business plan' for the rest of the year. By this, I assume he means how we intend to survive. As I have not yet discussed his proposal that we sell part or all of La Puce with my wife, I shall have to try and placate Mr Dette by unveiling and talking up my scheme for the elderflower champagne production. If nothing else, it will give him another opportunity to make a bad joke at our expense.

Donella having bullied me out of my long shorts and string vest and into a suit, we set out for the latest location of our itinerant bank account. In the last ten years, we have faithfully followed our bank manager on his travels, and taken our business with *Crédit Agricole* to five different branches.

At the moment, we are customers of their bank at La-Haye-du-Puits, which holds the record for having the most shops per population in Lower Normandy. This means it also holds the record for having the most shops shut at the same time, and usually when the most customers are in town. The bank at La-Haye-du-Puits is a major branch, and this means that Mr Dette is doing well on his career path, in spite of suffering the stigma of having us as customers.

In France, it is quite common for rising executives with big companies to be moved around to different departments and branches, but our manager seems more than usually mobile. I have always taken his constant movements about the peninsula as a good sign, as Mr Dette is obviously being groomed for stardom, which makes it a sensible idea to stay with him wherever he goes. My wife believes he is, in fact, moving so frequently at his own request, and to try and shake us off. Whatever the reason, we have certainly moved our meagre resources around the Cotentin more than the average international money-laundering cartel, and I think it has aroused suspicion at head office. The last time our bank manager went on holiday, we were called in for an interview with a very austere official, who said he was sitting in for Mr Dette and wanted to get to know the branch's foreign customers. He asked us all sorts of penetrating questions, mostly about how we made a living, why we kept so little money in our account, and particularly why we kept following the same manager around the bank's network. Afterwards, I said to Donella that it was nice to have a big bank showing such an interest in its smaller customers. She snorted and said that they were obviously interested because they thought we were involved in some sort of scam with Mr Dette, or had something on him and were blackmailing him to keep our account alive and overdraft facility in place.

The singular relationship between the major clearing banks in France and their foreign customers - particularly their British customers - has developed and become more complex with the increasing number of expatriates on their books. On the one hand, there is any bank's natural desire to take advantage of what must be, taken in total, a huge amount of business and income. On the other, there appears to be a natural reluctance to deal with some of the Britons who arrive with limited funds and unusual propositions for how they are going to make a living in their new home. Given some of the stories we have heard about rural bank managers being taken in by alleged British entrepreneurs, it is no wonder it can be so difficult to set up a bank account in France, and that signing a cheque for money you do not have can result in a prison sentence. This is another reason we shadow our indulgent if gallows-humoured bank manager so closely.

The journey to La-Haye-du-Puits was mostly uneventful, with only two relatively (for France) minor road accidents blocking the main carriageway south across the great central flood plain of the Cotentin. In Britain, I have observed that passing the scene of a crash seems to remind motorists of the dangers of bad driving, and that they will generally proceed much more calmly for at least a mile afterwards. In France, the opposite seems true, with the frustrated drivers hurtling madly away from the twisted metal, pools of blood and flashing lights as if intent on being the first to win the privilege of causing the next crash.

Arriving in good time to be politely late for our appointment with Mr Dette, we decided to visit the town's *dépôt de vente*, which is the biggest in the area. At the moment we have no need of an inflatable bouncy castle or a World War II German infantryman's helmet with a hole in it, but it is always fascinating to wander round the warehouse and see what unusual items are on offer. In our part of France, there are no bric-a-brac shops or used furniture stores, and people generally take any unwanted but remotely saleable household items to their nearest sales depot. After a long debate with the manager on what their family heirloom is worth on the open market, a compromise will be reached, a price chalked on the piece and

117

it will be put on show, with the depot taking a percentage when or if it is sold. What makes these storehouses so fascinating is the variety and contrast of goods on display. When we first visited the depot, it was not unusual to find a magnificent oak 18th century buffet sitting alongside a wonky self-assembly, chipboard-veneered sideboard. At a time when many young Norman families were busily discarding their great-grandparents' heirlooms in favour of more modern and less monumental furniture, the classic oak buffet might have been valued at not much more than the sideboard, or sometimes less. Nowadays and after regular raids from British and Parisian antique dealers who could not believe their luck, prices tend to be less eccentric, but there are still bargains to be found.

After touring the showrooms and resisting the urge to buy an engaging stuffed stoat, we found our old friend and haggling adversary the manager distressing a reproduction Louis XV wardrobe with a bicycle chain. Having exchanged the usual pleasantries and accounts of how down on our luck we each were, I asked him why there were so few customers on the premises. Pausing to wipe his brow and give the wardrobe a thoughtful kick, he explained that he was on his summer holidays and the depot was, in fact, closed for the next fortnight. He had come in to catch up on his work, but had left the doors open so he could have the pleasure of telling visitors that they could not come in.

We have arrived at the bank to find the foyer packed with a sea of clearly anxious customers. Such is the press that confusion reigns, and some people are actually queuing. Although it is approaching the lunchtime closure and today is market day, there is obviously something extraordinary going on, and the bank has clearly taken special measures to cope with the emergency by reducing the number of staff on duty.

Milling around the service desks are little old ladies

clutching paper bags stuffed with ancient banknotes, nervous-looking businessmen carrying bulging briefcases, and burly farmers who look as if they are waiting to have a tooth pulled without the option of anaesthetic. Then I see an assistant counting a huge pile of centimes as a severe-looking woman in a black dress and veil watches her like a hawk, and I realise what is happening.

This morning, the final plans for France's change of currency were announced. From the first day of the new year, the euro will be the official monetary unit, and the franc will be gradually withdrawn from circulation. People will still be able to use francs to pay for their goods for two months after the changeover, and will receive their change in euros. Theoretically, all should go smoothly and there will be no panic, especially with nearly nine months to go before the franc becomes extinct. But, for some reason, these people seem more than keen to pay cash in to their accounts.

Then, as I watch a farmer appear to wipe a tear from his eye as he hands a wad of crumpled and soiled notes across the counter, I understand the real reason for the furore. Because of its punitive tax system, France has probably the most extensive black economy in Europe. Two sets of books for any small business is the norm, and cash in the hand is much preferred to a cheque for any services rendered. There must be many billions of undeclared francs stashed in mattresses and under floorboards across the country, and they will all be worthless after the deadline. The real problem will come when the owners have to explain the sudden appearance of quite large sums of money when changing them into euros. Obviously, the bank is under siege from everyone with an undeclared nest-egg, and they have all hit upon the same idea of making a series of small deposits before E-day arrives. Being France, there will also be an undeclared amnesty to allow this process to happen, and billions of francs, centimes and perhaps even sous will be cascading into banks and building societies from now until the big changeover, but panic has already set in. The chaotic situation suits me well, as the longer I can delay our encounter with our bank manager, the longer I have to think up a convincing presentation of my financial plan for the coming year. But, in spite of the crush, we are moving steadily towards the counter, and just as I consider staving off the inevitable by feigning a heart attack, I am quite literally saved by the bell.

At first, I think the strident clanging is either a fire alarm, or a distress call for a medic to treat someone who has had a real seizure at the prospect of letting go of their secret hoard. But then, and as the crowd begin to disperse, I realise it is the bell to signal lunchtime closing.

Thankful for any chance to delay the moment of our encounter with Mr Dette, I shepherd Donella towards the exit. As we reach the glass doors, a whirring sound replaces the urgent clamour of the bell, and a metal grille drops suddenly from the ceiling. Following the remaining staff members out of a side door and into an alleyway, I realise that, in all my years of trying to avoid close contact with this particular institution, it is the first time I have actually been locked in rather than out of a bank.

Along with at least fifty customers who did not conclude their business before the end of the morning session, we have taken up residence in a bar opposite the bank. All around us sit anxious-looking people, most of whom are gazing intently at the metal grille while fingering an overstuffed purse, wallet or paper bag.

In for a long wait, we decide to pick up the ingredients for a pavement picnic. Last week, the main supermarket at La-Haye-du-Puits announced it was coming into line with other go-ahead European countries and modernising its approach to customer service by staying open through the traditional two hour lunch break. This bold new move not only infuriated the staff, but has clearly failed to impress the customers, so we are free to wander through the deserted aisles and make our selection of cheeses and crusty bread. As we leave, I see a sign declaring that the management has decided, after the experiment, to revert to its original opening (and especially closing) times.

Back at the bar, we push our way through a small but very noisy gathering of young people on the terrace who are clearly intent on making a nuisance of themselves. The girls are wearing skimpy tops and assorted pieces of jewellery through their ears, navels, noses, lips and eyebrows, and the equally pierced youths have cropped hair, tattoos and generally unpleasant expressions. Obviously enjoying the shocked looks of the customers around them, they are throwing cans of beer and lighted cigarettes at each other, and my heart sinks when I hear one of them shout an obscenity and realise that they are French, and not proper British hooligans.

Along with mobile phones, baseball caps and pop music, we seem to have begun exporting a fashion for the sort of oafish behaviour at which some British youngsters excel. When I remark on this escalating trend, my francophile friends say that I am worrying needlessly, and that it is against everything in the French culture for the young to behave as badly as their British counterparts. They may believe it is just a passing phase, but times and cultures change, and few people in England a generation or so ago would have believed how badly so many of our own youngsters would turn out. I hope my friends are right, but I cannot help but believe that, once this particular genie is out of the bottle, it will be impossible to persuade him back inside again, even in rural France.

Making a detour to avoid a confrontation with the yobs, we enter the bar and take the only free table. Our nearest neighbour is a preoccupied farmer, who merely grunts absent-mindedly when I comment on the crush. He is an elderly man, with a ruddy road map of a face and the standard rural uniform of a voluminous and extremely tatty jacket over green overalls and brown wellington boots, topped off with a cloth cap that looks as if it has been shaped by countless cycles of rain and sun to fit every detail and contour of his head. It would be interesting to know the last time he took his *casquette* off, but I do not like to ask him as he appears to be in deep reverie.

While I try to attract the waiter's attention by waving a large denomination note, the farmer grunts again, picks up his glass and raises one bushy eyebrow. He is obviously a regular, as the waiter materialises at his side before the eyebrow has settled back in place. The farmer sighs heavily, regards the tiny glass in his huge paw of a hand, then lifts it to his lips and tilts his head back to allow the few remaining drops of liquor inside to trickle into his mouth. When he is content that the glass is truly empty, he returns it to the table, looks at it reflectively, then nods. With a flourish, the waiter puts the neck of the bottle to the top of the glass, and his customer stares fixedly as the level of wine creeps slowly upwards. Such is the steady hand and skill of the waiter that not only does he fill the glass to the very brim, but actually manages to create a convex surface, thus adding infinitesimally to the quantity of wine served.

Satisfied that he has got his money's worth, the farmer grunts again, then reaches into the inside pocket of his jacket. Bringing out a bulging wallet, he unzips a pocket, rummages about with banana-like fingers, and finally extracts five small coins. As if saying goodbye for the last time to a dear friend, he holds the coins tightly for a moment, then lays them in a neat line on the table top. After a respectful pause, the waiter picks them up and hurries away. Such is our absorption with what is happening at the farmer's table, I completely forget to take the fleeting opportunity to order our drinks. Rather than risk picking up the glass and spilling a drop of his wine, the old farmer now inclines his head and sucks up the bonus bulge. Sitting back, he then regards the wallet in his hand solemnly before starting on what is obviously an important ritual.

Oblivious to us and anyone else in the bar, he opens

another section of the wallet and extracts a thick sheaf of soiled banknotes, which he places reverently on the table. He counts twelve of the notes out, then picks them up and counts them again. Then he reaches into a side pocket of his jacket, and pulls out a crumpled envelope. After putting the twelve notes into the envelope, he seals it, makes a mark on it with a stub of a pencil that has been nestling behind his ear, then puts the envelope away in one of the breast pockets of his jacket. After patting the pocket, he takes four more notes from the pile on the table, and another envelope is produced from his side pocket. The next sealing and marking ceremony completed, the envelope is tucked into yet another pocket, and the process is repeated four times. Then, the routine changes as he reaches into an inside pocket and takes out a purse. Picking up and counting out the five banknotes remaining on the table, he folds them neatly, and tucks them into the purse. As he begins to put it back in his pocket, he hesitates, puts the purse on the table and takes a reflective sip of wine. Then he re-opens the purse, teases out one of the notes, and, to my surprise, takes his cap off. At first I think he is paying his last respects to the note, but then see that there is another brown envelope tucked into the lining of the cap. The farmer takes the envelope out, carefully smoothes the banknote out on the table top, fits it into the envelope, then puts it back into the lining of his cap. The cap is returned to its familiar billet, the purse to the allotted pocket, and the farmer drains his glass. Giving a long and melancholy sigh, he stands, adjusts his cap again, pats all the pockets on his coat, then walks slowly towards the door.

As we watch through the window, he begins to walk across the road, taking each step as carefully and reluctantly as a man traversing a minefield. Reaching the pavement, he climbs the steps and arrives at the grill protecting the glass doors to the foyer of the bank. After regarding the locked entrance for a moment, he squares his shoulders, turns and walks almost jauntily back down the steps before making his way towards the market square.

While I continue to wave my money at the waiter, I say that the farmer must have seen that the grille was down and that the bank was still closed for lunch, so his ascent of the steps was pointless. My wife smiles and says I have, as usual, completely missed the point of this small epiphany. Of course the farmer knew that the bank was still closed. He clearly wished to savour the pleasure of being able to hang on to his hard-won francs for just a little longer.

We are back at La Puce, and I am in a much lighter frame of mind. This is not because we have had a successful meeting with the bank manager, but because there has been no meeting. Still under siege, Mr Dette sent a message to the front desk that he would not be able to see us, and asking if we would make an appointment for next month. It is a temporary reprieve, and will not solve any problems. But at least I have won a short breathing space.

Whatever happens, I must press on with my plans for the first batch of our elderflower champagne, try to make some headway on the new book, and to think of other ways of staving off financial disaster without selling our home. Clearly, we must try to make some drastic economies. Perhaps I will suggest to Donella that we could save a considerable amount on our grocery and corn bills if we were to eat rather than feed the Campbell gang. On the other hand, perhaps that would not be one of my more thoughtful suggestions.

...Nor all that glisters gold.

Thomas Grey, English poet (1716-71). From *Ode On The Death Of A Favourite Cat.*

NINE

The heat wave continues, and the season of fetes and forgetfulness draws ever closer.

At our regular Jolly Boys Club meetings, we are working hard on getting into physical and mental shape for the demands of a solid month of celebrating the arrival of the summer solstice.

My wife is still a martyr to every hungry or angry insect in the area, but she is now happily preoccupied with planning new additions to her menagerie. Today she is in exceptional mood, as she has two marriages to arrange, and Gert and Daisy are to be the brides.

All the books on the subject that I have read say that one cockerel will more than cope with a whole hen house. We have only two hens, but my wife is a great believer in fidelity within any union, and insists that Gert and Daisy should each have their own mate. Although our spinster hens seem perfectly happy exploring La Puce by day and devising and staging dramatic break-out attempts from their compound at night, Donella believes they will not be truly fulfilled until each has experienced the joys of motherhood. Or, in other words, begin to lay fertilised rather than sterile eggs. I would rather not run the risk of finding the odd beak or claw in my breakfast egg, but Donella is adamant. Consequently, she has arranged a visit to the home of a specialist English poultry breeder tomorrow, and plans to personally select the most suitable mates for Gert and Daisy. As the breeder is also a connoisseur of fine wines and keeps a locally renowned cellar, I have offered to go with her and help choose the most virile-looking cocks. My wife has agreed to me coming, but given my record for finding a mate for Ermintrude the goose, I have been ordered to leave the matchmaking strictly to her.

All may be quiet at the hen house for the moment, but there has been trouble in the skies above the big pond. This evening I watched from the caravan in the water meadow as an unusual territorial battle took place, and one which had a surprising outcome.

With the shadows growing longer and dusk approaching, I noticed our barn owl had taken up its favourite observation post on a branch of the blasted Hobbit Tree. A little later, a large black bird came flapping slowly across the meadow to settle at the top of one of the giant beech trees lining Hunters Walk. Although it was too far away for positive identification, I assumed it was one of the extended family of rooks that has been investigating the possibilities of setting up home with us. It is common knowledge in the countryside that rooks and crows will spend weeks surveying a potential nesting site, weighing up the food supply and potential competition, and moving in only if the locality meets their requirements. Knowing how my wife cares for all wild birds lucky enough to stumble upon La Puce, I am surprised we do not have at least a dozen teeming rookeries already.

As the dusk began to thicken, the two birds sat no more than a dozen yards apart, both apparently watching each other and the hunting ground below. Then an early moonshadow passed across the big pond, and I looked up to see, far above, what looked like our resident buzzard. He too had obviously arrived in search of supper. Not deigning to acknowledge its rivals, the king of the air came gracefully to rest on another riverside branch, and a peculiar Mexican stand-off began. None of the three predators would initiate recognition, and none would move on to another territory.

Then came a sudden movement in the long grass beyond the pond, and all three birds took to the air. At first I thought there would be a collision as they zeroed in on their mutual quarry, but each veered off at the last moment and returned to their separate roosts. After a few minutes of tense impasse, a harsh chorus signalled the arrival of reinforcements, and three dark shapes appeared through the growing gloom. Just as they arrived, another movement stirred the grass by the water's edge, and an explosion of activity followed. The buzzard soared into the air, hovered for a moment to take aim, and was promptly attacked by all four rooks. While the combatants wheeled and pitched and screeched above the pond, the owl slipped away from its perch, dropped to the grass, struck and disappeared with its prey.

Eventually, the buzzard gave way to superior numbers and limped off in search of a less fractious hunting ground, and the rooks flapped away into the night, their raucous victory cries echoing around the long reaches of the water meadow.

We have had an interesting evening at the home of the English poultry breeder.

Maurice and his wife Julie have lived in a village near St Sauveur for as long as we have been at La Puce, and are regarded by the locals as almost as eccentric. Together with his passions for solo morris dancing, and collecting, cataloguing and sampling every variety of wine produced in France, Maurice is also a keen cross-breeder of all varieties of fowl. With this hobby, he is a firm believer that bigger is better.

While not especially interested in his wine collection apart from helping him with the tastings, Maurice's wife is nearly as fanatical as Donella about animal welfare. She also seems to have the same knack for persuading animals not to behave as nature intended.

Fronting the square at the village of Cogasville, the couple's house is tastefully restored, opulently furnished and immaculately kept, while their back yard looks like the exercise deck of Noah's Ark on a particularly busy day. Within its confines, every sort of species seem to rub along quite happily. Goats, pigs, ducks, geese, rabbits and even baby foxes peacefully co-exist and break all the formal rules of nature, especially in the matter of who is supposed to eat whom. So cosseted and well-fed are they, that all seem to have forgotten their place in the food chain.

With such a bond, Donella and Julie are obviously the best of friends, and tend to spend any meeting enthusing about the psychological welfare and bowel movements of their flocks in the way that other women discuss the contents of their wardrobes.

We arrived at their yard to find Maurice pursuing what looked like a small peacock with chicken-like plumage and a startling red crown, while his wife was happily occupied in the shed with a rusty contraption of springs, levers and rows of vicious-looking teeth.

After catching and overpowering the giant rooster, Maurice explained that he was making great progress with his experiments, and that Julie was restoring a 19th-century mantrap she had picked up at a bargain price in the depot at La-Haye-du-Puits. When I asked if she was going to hang it on a wall as a reminder of past inhumanities, she replied quite casually that it would soon be in full working order and ready for action. When I laughed at what I thought was her joke, she looked at me blankly, then explained that there had been a confrontation with the local hunting club about a pair of fox cubs she had recently adopted. The club secretary had called yesterday to say that his members were happy that she was bringing the animals back to full health, as long as she was sure to let them know when and where they were to be released into the wild. The hunting party would then be in position and ready to enjoy the sport of shooting the vermin at point blank range, and would even be pleased to supply other orphans and sickly specimens for her to fatten up for the kill. If she insisted on keeping the foxes as pets, the secretary had hinted, there might well be a night-time visitation to their yard to dispose of them.

The mantrap was Julie's answer to the ultimatum, and she said that Maurice had added to the heated debate by offering to set his genetically modified monster chicken on any unwelcome visitors. Having seen the giant bird in action, I gauged it as even money which would be the most effective deterrent.

Leaving Donella to lend an enthusiastic hand with the restoration of the trap while discussing other and even more grisly ways of punishing humans (and especially men) cruel enough to harm defenceless animals, Maurice and I retired to inspect the latest additions to his wine cellar.

Some hours later, and we were to be found enjoying a drink in a local bar, with Julie having brought her mantrap along so she could make some final adjustments while she and my wife discussed the feasibility of installing central heating and power showers in their hen houses.

They had also brought the intended husbands of Gert and Daisy with them, so we had two bantam cocks in the company. Julie was a little tearful to be losing Fred and Barney, but acknowledged they were going to the best of homes, and wanted to take the opportunity to have a farewell drink with them. As they fluttered out of their carrying case and began exploring the bar, I was relieved to see that, unlike the giant mutant fowl, both birds were of approximately the same size as most chickens I have met, and only had one head apiece.

When Julie introduced us, I saw that Fred was the larger of the two, with a magnificent tail plumage of turquoise. He also had a set of extremely flared feathers on each leg which, together with his arrogant strut and gaudy colouring, reminded me of a particularly vain Latin-American *marimba* musician. Barney was quite diminutive and almost laid-back in comparison, and with his shoulder-swinging and ducking and weaving gait, reminded me of a small but supremely self-confident boxer. Perhaps that is why there is a bantam-weight division in the sport.

For birds which had been so obviously indulged by their mistress, they seemed well-behaved enough in company, and Maurice explained that he often took them on visits to the pub as they enjoyed the outing, and were quite fond of cider shandy with a dash of blackcurrant juice. The landlady had no objection, as she said Fred and Barney were generally better mannered, cleaner and made for more absorbing conversation than most of her male clientele.

As I felt the urge for a cigarette to go with my glass of wine, I remembered that, apart from its current customer profile, the bar is quite unusual, as it is probably the only non-smoking *tabac* in all Normandy - and, for all I know, perhaps in all France.

While the closure of yet another local store and bar is an almost weekly event in our area, Maurice and Julie's small village boasts two retail outlets, sitting conveniently on either side of our friends' house. At one end of the square, there is the general grocery store, bar and *tabac* run by a doughty woman of advanced years. On the other is an interesting bar and restaurant owned by an ever-smiling Turkish lady of a certain age, who has a huge and surprisingly young family.

As tends to be the way in rural France there are a number of complications and considerations to be taken into account when planning to do business at either bar. The elderly lady enjoys ill-health and is an asthmatic, so you may buy your packet of *Gitanes* at her shop but not smoke them there. The owner of the other bar is an enthusiastic smoker and lighting up is almost compulsory when on her premises, but she is not allowed to sell cigarettes. All smokers, including the owner of the rival establishment, must visit the *tabac* for their supplies, but then may only smoke them at the Turkish bar. Because they wish to support the only grocery store for miles and yet not lose a bar where they can enjoy a cigarette and a smile from the owner, the villagers have developed a strange protocol so that they can be - and be seen to be - fair to both businesses.

The first part of the time-honoured tradition and routine for local smokers (which means around 99% of the village) is quite straightforward. First, you drop into the *tabac* and buy your cigarettes, then walk across the square to the rival bar to order your drink and light up. Having emptied your glass, local custom and usage demand that you take it to be recharged at the *tabac*, and then exchange extended pleasantries and all the local gossip with Madame. The craving for another cigarette having taken hold, it is time to return to the Turkish bar with your empty glass, and start the process all over again. Local men are measured for their drinking capacity by the number of times they cross the square in a fairly straight line during any session, and it is a popular village story that an enterprising local individual once set up a shuttle service, running the most trenchant customers back and forth across the square on particularly rainy evenings. In our part of France, this would naturally have meant that his services were much in demand. The story goes that the facility ceased when the driver fell out with the local policeman over a lunchtime game of *pétanque,* and was stopped and breathalysed in the middle of his last hundred metre journey of the evening. It is a nice tale, but I do not think it could really have happened, not even in the Cotentin.

As a result of our visit, Maurice told me he was confident that a new village record has been established for traversing the square in a single session, and the promenade also gave us the opportunity to take the prospective bridegrooms of Gert and Daisy for a walk. Though they are quite used to seeing unusual sights in our neck of the woods, the frequent reappearance of four middle-aged English settlers accompanying two bantam cocks back and forward across the square while struggling to carry a partly-restored mantrap must have provided passing locals with a rich vein for further village tales.

Donella's matchmaking plans have not gone smoothly, and I think that one of our new bantam cocks may be gay, or at least asexual.

When we arrived back at La Puce, we followed Maurice's advice and put the two cockerels together outside the hen house after locking Gert and Daisy inside. As he had explained, this would allow Fred and Barney to size up the situation, and work out their own particular pecking order in the new environment. We were not to worry, he said breezily, if the two cocks had a bit of a punch-up. It was all quite normal, and it was unlikely they would do each other much damage. Despite Donella's reservations, I insisted we should give the two males the opportunity to sort out who was to be the top dog, or in this case, top cock. It was, as I said, only like two young men about to go into a disco deciding who would have first choice of the available talent.

Accordingly, we took the cocks from their carrying box, and set them down facing each other. For a moment, there was no reaction as they looked at us and their new surroundings, and then a muffled and somehow seductive clucking from inside the hen house triggered off the action. Cocking his head to one side and staring at the door to the coop, Fred scratched the ground as if sharpening his claws in readiness, threw back his head and let our a strident crow, then charged towards his rival. Barney, who had seemed, if anything, disconcerted by our hens' siren calls, immediately turned tail and fluttered frantically up to the safety of a nearby hazel tree.

After an hour of trying to coax him down with reassuring words and handfuls of maize, Donella went off to collect some blankets and our camping mattress so she could keep him company during his first night at La Puce. Meanwhile, I opened the door of the hen house to allow Fred in to commence what I doubt, in spite of my wife's wishes, will be a strictly monogamous relationship with either Gert or Daisy.

Another of my wife's attempts to impose human morals upon members of her menagerie has come unstuck. This is most unusual, and an obvious disappointment to her. Firstly, there has been the continuing failure to persuade the two new bantam cocks to pair off with our hens. Despite my wife giving Barney a daily grooming and encouraging him to join in their daily expeditions around La Puce, he remains resolutely aloof from Fred and his small harem, and prefers to spend his time scratching around the terrain on his own. As dusk falls, Fred and his consorts rush eagerly back to their love nest, while Barney flutters up to spend a solitary night in the hazel tree.

Donella's plan to segregate Ermintrude the goose and the two female ducks from the rapacious Campbell gang has also been a costly waste of time and effort. After I had dug the new pond and erected and furnished the shed by the grotto, my wife spent days trying to persuade the three birds of the advantages of moving to their new, all-female facilities. Then, no more than an hour after she had finally got them locked in for the night, we heard a tremendous racket, and arrived to find the male Campbells and Gladstone the giant mallard laying siege to the refuge, and Blanche and Hen making as much noise inside.

When my wife finally conceded defeat and opened the door, the females dutifully followed the males back to the big pond and their life of subjugation and constant sexual abuse. I had hoped that I would be able to claim the new shed for myself, but Donella has now decided it should be fitted out as luxurious bachelor quarters for Barney, the gay bantam.

I think I may have been wrong about Barney's sexual orientation. This morning, I saw him digging a dust bath by the wooden bridge, and a little later I found Daisy enjoying it. Then he appeared from behind the ruined end of the mill cottage with a fat, wriggling worm in his beak. He dropped it casually beside the bath, then strolled off without a backward glance.

Rather than having no interest in the hens, I think he has been playing a waiting game, and had deferred to the much bigger Fred to avoid a potentially fatal confrontation. Perhaps my wife is right that animals can be much cleverer than humans when it comes to getting their own way, and Barney is a lover rather than a fighter.

Walking from the mill cottage to the caravan in the water meadow this morning, I almost stepped on what I thought was a large green-brown chicken turd, so stopped to take a closer look.

It is not that I am particularly interested in chicken droppings, although they do come in some interesting shapes and textures and designs. It is just that the colour and consistency can tell the observer much about the health and therefore contentment of the former owner. An ice cream-like white whorl on the top denotes peak condition, which bodes well for the quality and frequency of eggs. I have a special interest at this time, of course, as the recent arrival of Fred and Barney could well have had an effect on the mental and physical condition of our hens and their egg production rate. Picking the object up for closer inspection, I found that it had a slimy and strangely hard exterior, and also that it moved. Having dropped it in shock, I then saw a pair of small claws waving feebly, and realised that I had not stumbled across the evacuations of a sick chicken, but a very sick crayfish.

As I picked it up again, I noticed a glint of pale gold a little further along the path and close to the edge of the big pond, then saw it was a dead goldfish. There were only two conclusions to be drawn. Either the creatures had been dropped separately by a poacher and a heron, or they had made their own way to where I found them. Freshwater crayfish do travel across land, and like to territorialise any stretch of water in the area, but this one was high and dry, and had been moving away from the nearest pond or stream rather than towards it. Psycho and his rapidly diminishing tribe are truly exceptional goldfish, but I don't think even they have developed the instinct or ability to traverse dry land. I had not seen our heron since he was frightened off by the male ducks, so the only conclusion I could reach was that the crayfish was on the run from the big pond, trying to escape from the Campbell gang, and the goldfish had leapt out of the pond in sheer desperation to try and join it. Natural historians will tell you that crayfish are not a dish of choice for ducks, but they, of course, have not met the Campbells.

Finding some old netting in the feed store and cutting a branch from a hazel tree, I rigged up a crude boom across one corner of the pond, and gently lowered the crayfish in to what would hopefully be a duck-free environment. Then I went to tell Donella about the desperate breakout from the big pond, and to discuss how we can save our once-thriving cray and goldfish tribes from extinction.

Our mercy mission is over, and a number of the dwindling band of goldfish and crays have been shipped to a place of safety. We have spent the morning with net, bucket and wheelbarrow, shuttling back and forth between the pond and the grotto. With its steep banks and crashing cascade, it is too dangerous a place for even the Campbells, so the remnants of Psycho's tribe should be safe there. Some goldfish and most of the crayfish will obviously have eluded our sweep of the big pond, but they will have to take their chances there until I can persuade Donella that the male ducks should be either culled or given away.

As we poured the last bucketful of fish, crays and pond water into what is in reality a tree-lined and overgrown basin rather than a grotto, I felt someone watching me, and looked up to see our nosey neighbour Mr Trefle standing on the far bank. Following the usual exchange of false pleasantries, he scratched his long nose, rubbed his jaw a couple of times, then asked me if I made a habit of shifting water about my land by the bucketful. Personally, he said, he had always found that it moved quite easily along rivers without any help. Thinking quickly, I made a big show of looking around, then announced quite casually that I had been panning for gold. After putting his hand to his eyebrows as if about to poke his eyes back in to their sockets, he turned away, smothered a guffaw, then looked back at me with the classic expression of a French countryman who thinks you are pulling his leg, but is worried you may not be, especially when the subject under discussion is anything of monetary value.

Inviting him to cross the gravestone bridge, I sat him

down on the bench by the grotto and made him promise on what he held most dear in the world not to reveal what I was about to tell him. After thinking for a while, he swore on his tractor that what I had to say would go no further, and was obviously so shaken by the thought of there being gold on the land on which he had trespassed for years that he offered me a cigarette.

After lighting the foul roll-up and pausing to cough and choke mostly for dramatic effect, I told him that a holidaying British geologist had stayed with us last week, and had said that the combination of ores and minerals he had seen while walking along Hunters Walk made it almost certain that there was gold to be found on our land. The last time he had seen such a potentially rich terrain, I said he said, was when he had visited the scene of the great Californian Gold Rush. Unfortunately, he did not think that there would be any actual nuggets lying around the place, especially given what he had heard about Norman farmers and how they loved to nose around on other people's property, but he was sure the stream at La Puce would yield rich pickings if we went about it in the right way.

Consequently, we had spent this afternoon panning the stream alongside Hunters Walk with my bucket and Donella's old garden sieve, and Mr Trefle had caught us in the act. Disappointingly and after several hours of hard work, we had found nothing more than a handful of tiny fragments of what could be gold, so were giving up the search. The geologist was probably mistaken in his judgement, though he had said that the masses of broken branches, leaf mould and general debris slowing the stream down might well prevent any decent-sized deposits being washed up from the bed. As Mr Trefle absent-mindedly offered me another cigarette, I said that we did not have the time or energy to clear the stream, even if there were anything of value to be found in it, but would not want the word to get out and start a gold rush on our land.

Having assured me that our secret was safe with him, Mr Trefle said that, if I had no objection, he would continue his stroll along Hunters Walk, and might even spend a few moments pulling the odd dead branch from our stream. They would more than probably be too saturated to make a decent fire, but helping a friend keep his land and waterways in good order was the least that a good neighbour could do.

The goldfish and crays having appeared to settle quite happily in the grotto, we played sudden death killer dominoes in the cottage till after dark, then took a stroll to the mill garden to say goodnight to the chickens. My wife was pleased to see that Barney seemed happy in his new quarters, but surprised to find the egg that had been missing from the hen house this morning nestling in the corner of the shed. She said that Daisy had probably been confused and returned to the wrong place for her morning lay, but after what I have seen her and Barney getting up to when Fred is not around, I suspect Daisy knew exactly what she was doing.

As we sat by the grotto and tried to count the stars in just one tiny corner of the vast Norman sky, Donella said she thought she could see a light at the far end of Hunters Walk, and suggested we get the broken shotgun and try to surprise any trespassers. I assured her that what she had seen could only have been a will o' the wisp. Who, after all, would have any reason for splashing about in our stream at this hour? It was not as if, I said, that there was anything of the remotest value to be found in the muddy waters of the Lude, at any time of day or night.

We cannot bring ourselves to believe it possible that a foreigner should be in any respect wiser than ourselves. If any such point out to us our follies, we at once claim those follies as the special evidences of our wisdom.

Anthony Trollope, English novelist (1815-82), in *Orley Farm* (1862).

TEN

High summer has arrived, and La Puce is in full bloom.

The hedgerows and trees are ripe with promise, and I have already picked a sackful of elderflowers for our Champagne of the Flea. Gert and Daisy and their respective spouses now spend long and obviously contented days exploring every corner of the terrain, and devising new ways of breaching the wire-mesh fence I have built around Donella's vegetable patch. Whatever else we may lack come autumn, we shall not be short of potatoes, beans, onions, corn, sprouts, cabbages, turnips, parsnips, pumpkins and especially, I realised this morning, marrows.

For the past month, we have watched in disbelief as the dainty green fingers of hundreds of what we had thought were courgettes grew to the size of the Widow of Négreville's forearms, and still they expand. This morning, I went through the empty seed packets in the greenhouse, and realised that I should have worn my spectacles when buying them. I should also have remembered that French for courgette may be *courgette*, but French for marrow is *courge*.

After a rough headcount, I estimated we will have more than enough marrows to see us through the next three years at normal consumption rate, as there are only so many things one can do to make that vegetable interesting enough to eat. At least, they will provide valuable bartering material, as long as I can persuade the local chefs that stuffed marrow was a great favourite of the ancient Vikings, and therefore a worthy addition to their menus of strictly traditional Norman fare.

Having confessed my cock-up to Donella, I walked along Hunters Walk to offer Mr Trefle a cup of tea and some words of encouragement with his gold-panning activities, then went to the mill cottage to see if, along with the information on producing Olde English Elderflower Champagne, my brew-it-yourself book offers any interesting recipes for marrow wine.

We have arrived at the Flaming Curtains to recover from our weekly visit to the supermarket.

If that is possible, the French seem to drive their shopping trolleys with more abandon than their cars. I have read that trolley rage is on the increase in British supermarkets, but from what I have seen in our part of Normandy, the most selfish and inconsiderate English housewife is not a patch on her French counterpart when it comes to steering a *chariot* with little due care and even less concern.

Unlike in Britain, however, sharp exchanges and confrontations are rare, as no quarter is asked or given, and no malice held by the loser of any encounter. To see normally well-mannered citizens entering the fray in a French supermarket would make, I think, the storming of the Bastille seem a very tame affair by comparison. Using your trolley as a

140

battering ram against the backs of the legs of the customer in front when movement at the checkout is too slow for your liking is standard practice. Rather than bring any rebuke, it merely encourages the injured party to do the same to the next customer in line, causing an immediate shunting-up of the queue. Bruised calves and even the imprint of the trolley manufacturer's name on one's thigh are an occupational and unconsidered hazard of any supermarket visit in our area. Behaviour that would cause a heated exchange in any branch of Somerfield goes unnoticed in any Super U, and I believe lessons in the most effective way to cause a logjam in any aisle must be taught in domestic science lessons at every French school. The most common cause is when two friends meet and stop for a lengthy chat, having carefully arranged their trolleys at right angles to the flow of traffic, completely sealing off the entire aisle until they decide to move on, or a third party smashes cheerfully through.

Today, though, a more dramatic example of our cultural differences was to take place as we waited with leg muscles tensed nervously at the checkout.

Hearing a commotion and the sound of angrily raised voices from the electrical goods and music aisle, I turned to see a large man apparently trying to choke the life out of a small youth. As the other shoppers looked on unconcernedly, the big man shook the lad enthusiastically before throwing him amongst a display of toasters. Dragging him up by the scruff of the neck, he then frogmarched his victim out of the store. As I made to go and help restore order, I caught the eye of the checkout girl, who calmly smiled, shook her head, then picked up a nearby phone.

Outside, the man had by now pulled a long baton from inside his jacket, and was belabouring the youth around the shoulders. As he screamed and wriggled, several people walked past with their trolleys, apparently unconcerned about the assault, and I even saw one elderly lady nod encouragingly at the man, then indicate with a mime how he could use his stick more effectively.

Then, a siren heralded the arrival of a police car, which squealed to a stop and disgorged two burly gendarmes. As they ran to the scene of the assault, the man stopped beating the boy, but rather than disarm and arrest him, the tallest of the two policemen nodded a friendly greeting and shook his hand cordially. After they had shared a cigarette with the assailant, both policemen shook his hand, then dragged the sobbing youth to the car, bundled him inside and sped away.

When I looked quizzically at the checkout girl, she said that the youth was a well-known shoplifter, and the large man an undercover security guard. He had obviously caught the young man stealing from the music section, and taken the necessary action. While she waited for Donella to sign the cheque, the girl added that she had heard the English were very soft on criminals and that it was getting that way in Paris, but here in the countryside, they still knew the best way to deal with hooligans and thieves. One thing was for certain; the youth's bruises would heal quickly, he had been exposed as a common *voleur* in front of the community, and he would not return to the scene of his crime in a hurry.

Wheeling our trolley back to the car, I asked my wife how she felt about the way the youth had been treated. After thinking for a moment, she said that there were obviously some areas where we could learn from our nearest continental neighbours, and besides, it could be argued that anyone stupid enough to want to steal French pop records deserved a good thrashing to knock some sense into him.

It was no great surprise to find Cameron sitting at the bar of the Flaming Curtains, nor to learn he is shortly to make a bigamous marriage.

When his new creative routine started, he said he worked much better and could think more freely if he was not chained to the computer in his room, so had decided to employ someone to write his thoughts down and type them up later. I know his new assistant speaks as little English as he does French, and that he forgot to bring the monitor screen for his computer when he came to Normandy, so it will be interesting to see how his novel turns out when it is finally printed.

From my observations during the past month, it seems to me that Cameron is lonely, and looking for someone to care for and about him, which is probably why he has proposed to each of the three secretaries he has so far employed. He claims each has been madly in love with him, but the relationship seems to last no more than a chapter of his book. His latest assistant seems a strange choice, even by Cameron's standards.

Mirabelle is a slim, husky-voiced young woman, and not unattractive, but she is the female equivalent of the mournful folk singer who regularly empties the bar at the Flaming Curtains, and, if possible, even more morose. She specialises in limp clothing, hair and posture, and works hard on presenting a face full of tragedy to her audience at all times. In many ways, she reminds me of our own dear Princess Diana. I know Mirabelle's role model is Edith Piaf, but I find her voice even more thin and reedy, and her self-composed songs even more despairing than the Little Sparrow at her most depressed.

As his latest amanuensis took a break to go and cast a shadow over a smiling young couple sitting in the corner, Cameron ordered the drinks and told us he was sure he had found true and eternal love this time. He believes Mirabelle and he are on a common spiritual plane, and both recognise and reject the banal values of an uncaring and shallow world. Now that they are together, they will spend the rest of their lives living in simple contentment in her cottage in the forest. There, she will compose great songs about Life and how awful it is, and he will write his novels on a similar theme. They will be a constant inspiration and comfort to each other, and he plans to pay for an album of her songs to be produced and marketed throughout France. I did not wish to spoil his mood by suggesting that the best way to market Mirabelle's songs would be as tapes for bar owners to play at closing time, or when they are fed up and want to have an early night. I also did not mention that she is his third life soulmate in less than a month.

For all his exhibitionist behaviour, I think Cameron is at heart a shy, lonely and unhappy man. He is a *faux*-eccentric, and works hard at trying to appear a free spirit, but I believe he is really quite normal. With his Steeleye Span tee-shirt and Celtic symbol earring, he reminds me of the sort of man who has his own pewter tankard at the local pub, drinks what he calls 'real' ale with gusto, sings revolutionary songs at closing time, then goes off to the office quite happily next morning. Despite his contrivances to appear apart from the crowd, Cameron is obviously searching for something stable in his life, and I hope he finds it before it is too late.

As we mumbled our congratulations, he commanded that Coco break out the champagne to celebrate his engagement, and asked if our host would set up the microphone so that Mirabelle could entertain the customers with a song that she had written specially for the occasion. As Coco and I exchanged glances, I suggested to my wife that we join the British Settlers Club table before the entertainment started and all the seats outside the Flaming Curtains were suddenly occupied.

In the way of these things, some hours have passed as a casual visit to our favourite local developed into a full-blown debating session, and afternoon has somehow drifted into late evening. This is a common occurrence in rural France. Nowadays, hardly a week goes by without a new face appearing at our British settlers' table, and most incomers have an unusual story to tell about their reasons for moving to

Normandy, and their plans for making a life and living here.

One of our newest members is an architect with permanently trembling hands who left England and his business in a hurry after causing a block of council flats to be built the wrong way round. As he said, it was a mistake anyone could have made, especially after a heavy night in a wine bar, but particularly unfortunate as the front doors of all the flats, which were meant to be a safe haven for single parents with young children, now open directly on to a busy dual carriageway.

The cack-handed architect, who is called Dexter, came to the Flaming Curtains as he had heard of our little club, and wanted to take advice from Cameron. His former business partner has already tracked him down, and there has been a terse exchange of letters. When Dexter wrote to say that he was in France seeking a special medicine, his ex-partner wrote back to say that, as far as he knew, all varieties of French wine were available in the UK, and that he should return to take his medicine in the courts. However, our new member is determined to start quite literally with a clean sheet, and plans to set up business in the area. He is already in the process of gaining permission to convert an old *manoir* on the outskirts of Bricquebec into trendy studio flats, which he hopes to sell to a mixture of local people and British visitors in search of a low-maintenance holiday or retirement home. I hope for the buyers' sakes that he will design the premises the right way round this time, as the building has magnificent views over the castle, but backs on to the council rubbish tip.

A steady drizzle is falling with the dusk, but such is our quiet contentment that nobody moves from the club table. It is now at that stage of any get-together of British expatriates that talk inevitably turns to news from across the Channel, and for us all to agree that Britain is going to the dogs, and how much happier we all are to be living in a foreign country. At this particular gathering, I feel that most of us mean what we say.

Unnoticed, the drizzle has become a quite heavy downpour, and as I return to the bar to order the drinks, I see Coco looking curiously at our party through the window alongside the terrace. When I walk in, he shakes his head and asks why we should choose to sit outside, especially as Mirabelle has at last finished her tribute to Cameron. In Normandy, he says, only fools and particularly stupid farm animals stay out in the rain when there is shelter to hand. I reply that he still has a lot to learn about the British. However much we love our new place of residence, there are still some things we miss about the old country, and sitting in the rain on a summer's day reminds us all of being on holiday at the seaside.

Every week seems to bring another boatload of Britons planning to buy a home or settle in our area, but there is still no sign of a single potential customer for the farmhouse at La Puce. I shall phone our agent at Port Rabine and ask if he has actually advertised the property, or has decided for some snobbish reason he does not want us on his books.

Today, I managed to avoid another long session of sitting in front of a blank screen by suggesting my wife and I go on a tour of British-held properties in the area and see how the owners are getting on with their various restoration projects. We might be able to help with some constructive advice on the work in hand, and the day would be a great help in giving me further material and inspiration for the new book. I know Donella likes to lend a hand or give advice to those newcomers who need it, and I also enjoy seeing new owners fulfilling their dreams. To be honest, when I am in such a low state, it also cheers me up to see people making even more of a mess of their building plans than even I did.

Our first call was at a former pig farm which its current owner believes will soon become a luxurious holiday village. As we wandered about the sprawling collection of roofless barns and corrugated-iron styes, he was obviously seeing something that I could not, even by shutting my eyes and stretching my imagination to the very limit.

After explaining how each sty would become a characterful and compact *gîte*, he showed us the slurry pit which would shortly metamorphosise into an olympic-sized, solar-heated swimming pool, and the dank cellar which would be transformed into a sophisticated wine bar. His budget for the conversion seemed wildly optimistic, but he said he will make great savings by doing the work himself. So far, he admitted, he had attempted no more than some basic DIY jobs at their executive estate home in Croydon; but he was confident that, with a little practice, he would soon be able to match the best efforts of the unreliable and expensive local craftsmen. His fervour for such totally unrealistic plans came as no surprise, as Ozzy is one of the legion of former white-collar workers who hanker after getting their hands dirty and doing some real work in their later years, and who believe they will gain spiritual fulfilment and inner peace by knocking a ruin in France about. I hope that, in future years, visitors will not look upon his mighty works and despair.

In spite of his enthusiasm, I noticed his wife kept her arms crossed firmly across her breast as we walked around the site, and that she wore a constant expression of grim resignation. I think she had seen their future, and her forecasts are far different from his shining vision. I wished them both good fortune with their project, and as we bumped away up the potholed track, I said to Donella that I hoped that their funds and marriage will survive the strain of the coming months.

Our next visit was to an isolated farmhouse owned by another former professional person, but one who has become a master of all building trades. Roger is an ex-schoolteacher who has not only taught himself all the skills needed for restoring his property, but become totally obsessed with doing every stage of the project himself.

Since he bought the derelict property ten years ago, his visits from England have become ever more frequent and longer, and he is now a virtual recluse. His life's mission is to completely rebuild and furnish the ancient building with his own hands, and he bitterly resents any distraction. His building materials and groceries are ordered by phone and delivered to the bottom of the track, and his neighbours say he has not left the building for several months. They also say he works late into the night seven days a week, and that his manic behaviour is causing much resentment locally as so many wives are now demanding that their husbands show a fraction of his enthusiasm for improving the family home. The only time I have had anything like a lengthy discussion with him was when he told me about the nine separate filters on his septic tank, and how each one worked.

When we arrived and persuaded him to let us on to the premises for the five minutes it would take for the animal glue he was boiling to reach exactly the right consistency, he told us his wife had called that morning to say she had found someone else and was leaving him. As we offered our embarrassed condolences, he said that it was not particularly bad news, as she had been planning to come over for a whole month later in the year, and her presence would have held him up no end. Besides, over the years and unlike my own wife, she had proved useless at heavy manual work, and even, despite her cake-making abilities, completely unable to make a decent mixer-full of cement.

A congenial end to our day when we dropped in to see some old friends who have been unrestoring their isolated cottage for the past decade. As we stumbled across a mound of brick debris and passed through any number of doorless openings, we saw Simon busily demolishing what looked like a perfectly respectable staircase, leaving his wife Susie stranded on the landing above.

After finding a stepladder so she could come down and open a bottle of wine, he cheerfully agreed that he was much better at knocking things down than restoring them, and had discovered a real talent for demolition work. Each visit, he would start a new project in a different part of the cottage, then get bored and start wielding a sledgehammer in another area of the premises.

Sitting on the terrace at a three-legged table his wife had rescued from the former kitchen, we watched the sun dip below a line of oak trees in the far distance, and talked about the benefits of their singular approach to the restoration of a French holiday home. As Simon said, they had no intention of ever living in France, and were perfectly happy in their comfortable house in the south of England. Beating up the cottage was their only real indulgence, and there were a number of advantages to their deconstruction project. For a start, they would never have to buy any expensive building materials, or beg elusive tradesmen to repair leaking plumbing systems or badly-installed electrical circuits. Also and unlike any other owners in the area, they were never worried about their holiday home being burgled, or damaged by storms or floods in their absence. Any acts of God might even leave the house in a better condition than it was. Best of all, they always had a good excuse when friends in England asked if they could stay at their holiday cottage. Some time in the future, perhaps, they would think seriously about making the place habitable, but for the moment, everything was going along just fine.

Pondering on the events of the day as we drove back to La Puce, I realised that I was no nearer to coming to a rational conclusion about the hundreds of Britons we hear from every year about their dreams of buying a home in France, or to even guess whether each of them will be happy to achieve their heart's desire. For some, the dreams match up to the realities, and sometimes, even more so. For others, the ambitions would perhaps be better left unfulfilled.

As we turned off the road and rolled down the track towards the welcoming lights of the mill cottage, I called to mind the old Arab caution about the perils of realising one's dearest wish. To have done so and found such happiness and contentment, my wife and I must be a fortunate couple indeed.

In spite of our parlous financial situation, the lack of progress on my new book and the pressing need to make a start on the brewing of our Elderflower Champagne of The Flea, my wife has announced that we are going to Wales to look at a dog.

When I said that there are literally thousands of dogs on permanent display in the area, Donella told me that a woman who runs a smallholding near Fishguard had called to say she has rescued a maltreated sheepdog, but cannot keep it. Despite having to take a very practical view of animal husbandry in order to survive on her fourteen acres of Welsh hillside, the woman obviously shares Donella's affection for creatures which are down on their luck. According to her, she and her husband liberated the animal from its cruel and drunken former owner last month, and she is nursing it back to health. Sadly, she will not be able to keep the dog, as her husband has insisted that the seven other collies she has accumulated over the years are more than capable of controlling their flock of six sheep. As a reader of my books and when considering who would give the dog the love and indulgence it deserved, she had naturally thought of my wife.

All my objections to travelling through three countries and each way across the English Channel were countered by Donella, who said I could not go on grieving for my beloved

Lucky for ever, and it would not be a betrayal to him to take on and give my love to another dog.

After a while, I agreed to at least consider her proposal, and went to sit and think beneath the Hobbit tree, where my darling Lucky sleeps in peace forever.

In spite of my reservations, I know Donella is right that it is time I pulled myself together. It is almost three years since Lucky died in my arms, and now we have returned to La Puce, I miss having him at my heels and in my heart more than ever, and any sensible person knows that a walk in the countryside is not a walk without a dog to share it.

Since our return, never a day has passed without my visiting the shattered elm tree on Hunters Walk which was Lucky's favourite resting place in summertime. I still miss him, will always love him and never forget the joys we shared together, but, as my wife says, it would be good to see a dog running free at La Puce again.

After telling him that he will always hold a special place in my heart and that any new dog will not be a patch on him, I walked back up the pathway to the cottage to tell my wife that I agreed with her proposal, and that, somehow, I believe Lucky was pleased to hear the news. As my wife said, a dog's love is unconditional, and my old friend loved me so much that he would want me to be happy with a new one.

Into the face of the young man who sat on the terrace of the Hotel Magnifique at Cannes there has crept a look of shame, the shifty, hangdog look which announces that an Englishman is about to talk French.

PG Wodehouse, *The Luck of the Bodkins* (1935).

ELEVEN

Following an expensive visit from an extremely patronising technician, my writing machine is working again. Like every other computer specialist I have dealt with, he obviously considered me mentally retarded because I didn't understand more than a fraction of what he was talking about, and I am sure he charged me extra just because I said that it was, after all, only a machine. Now I have no excuse for not working on the new book, and I am hoping that the visit to Wales will break my writer's block.

While Donella prepared for the journey and before leaving for today's JBC meeting, I walked along Hunters Walk to see if Mr Trefle had given up his search for gold in our stretch of the waters of the Lude. I found him at the boundary of our land, up to his knees in the stream and hard at work with a washing-up bowl, using what looked like a pair of his wife's old tights for a sieve. They may equally well have been a pair of *his* old tights, as many of the older men in our commune like to wear them under their trousers in the coldest winter months. If of the heaviest construction, they are as effective as standard woollen longjohns, and much cheaper. Last year, some tight-wearing males in the area took advantage of a special offer on pairs of World War II camouflage stockings that our general dealer Didier had found, but it was generally agreed by the men who tried them that the rusty metal suspender belts were extremely uncomfortable.

From his guarded greeting and instant denial when I asked if he had had any luck, I suspected my neighbour had already discovered the handful of gold-painted gravel with which I seeded the stream in his absence yesterday afternoon. I was pleased to see that he has already cleared a huge amount of debris from the Lude, then noticed the strips of sticking plaster on his face. When I asked him if he had cut himself shaving, he scowled and asked if I knew that we had a ferocious wildcat on our land. He said he had returned to continue with his neighbourly stream-clearing activities after dark last evening, and was set upon by the creature. I laughed, and said he has merely encountered our pet cat, Cato. As I turned to leave and pretended to see something glittering beneath a tangle of dead branches blocking a bend in the stream, he muttered darkly about letting the local hunting club know about our mad pet. I countered by explaining that Cato is more than just a half-feral cat, and we have good reason to believe her to be descended from the legendary werewolf that is said to have roamed La Puce centuries ago. Any hunters foolish enough to trespass on our land would therefore need to be loaded with silver bullets rather than buckshot if they wished to survive an encounter. They would also run the risk of a meeting with my wife, and he must know that, given her view of the local hunting fraternity, they would probably fare better with the werecat.

To give him something else to think about, I said I hoped his wounds would heal quickly, then casually remarked on how thick his eyebrows seemed to have grown since we last met, and asked if he had experienced any overwhelming urges for raw meat since the attack. I also pointed out that a full moon is due, so if I hear of any mutilated sheep being found in the neighbouring fields, I will know at whom to point the finger.

Even after all these years, I am still having trouble in getting to grips with the French language. When we moved across the Channel, I assumed I would somehow absorb fluency through a process of osmosis. It didn't work that way, but there is another natural method of feeling at ease with a foreign tongue. As any holidaymaker knows, the ability to converse easily in the *lingua franca* improves in direct ratio to the amount of alcohol consumed. In wine there may be truth, but there is also a measure of temporary fluency. Nowadays, most of my communication problems in Normandy still occur when I am completely sober, and quite often when the person with whom I am speaking is not deliberately misunderstanding what I am trying to say.

On the way to the club meeting I remembered that Donella had been too busy to make me breakfast, so diverted to the bakery shop in our rival village of St Jacques. Though I would never admit it in the hearing of any member of our commune, I believe the chocolate bread made there to be the best in our region, and perhaps even all Normandy.

Seeing some glowingly fresh almond *croissants* in the window, I went in and asked for a couple, jokily saying I had a sudden fancy to get my teeth into a hot almond. The lady owner looked at me strangely for a moment, shrugged, said that everyone had their own tastes and my inclinations were my own affair, then asked me if I wanted to buy anything. After repeating my error, I realised that, though the pronunciation may be very similar to English ears, in Normandy, and probably elsewhere in France, the word for 'almond' (*amande*) is quite distinct from the word for 'German' (*allemand*).

Still crunching my hot German, I have arrived at the Bar Ghislaine, and the first item on our debating agenda is the latest state of the betting on who is to become the new mayor of Néhou.

The elections take place next month, and there are just two candidates. The general consensus is that there is little to choose between them, and that they have certainly not been very imaginative with their rival manifestos. Apart from the usual promise to fight to the death any threat to local hunting rights, each has also pledged to clean up the village by cracking down on drug peddling, prostitution, street muggings and mobile phone theft, and to adopt a zero tolerance to petty offences like vandalism and illegal parking. As our resident philosopher Jacques Délabré says, the level of all sorts of criminal activity in the neighbourhood is below zero, and nobody owns a mobile phone. There are also no yellow lines in the village, and the only parking offence anyone can remember was when our local bobby brought his official moped into the bar with him after a spectacular D-Day veterans reunion. In future, Jacques concludes, prospective mayors for our village would do better taking the time to invent their own manifesto rather than copying the standard version used in big cities like Paris.

Next, it is time to move on to foreign affairs, and some of the members become very excited when I read them a summary of a report in a recent edition of the *Daily Telegraph*. The story is about a farmer in Suffolk who is receiving more than a hundred thousand pounds a year in subsidies for his crops of sugar beet and rape. In the article, the farmer agrees quite happily that his land and local climate are unsuitable for both crops, and that sugar beet production in England only began because of fears of a blockade shortage in the Napoleonic wars. Next year, he adds, he is going over to set-aside, as this will require less work and yield more profit.

When I explain that the set-aside system basically means farmers being paid for *not* growing any crops on a parcel of land, Miguel the flat-faced plasterer immediately suggests that we should write to Brussels and apply to take part in the scheme. As he points out, most of our members have been setting aside their gardens for years with no thought of profit, and would be happy to continue doing so if the price was right. As Miguel lives in a caravan in the middle of a field which has not been worked for years, he obviously likes the idea of becoming rich by leaving it exactly as it is.

The final item for discussion is the news that a British couple have bought an impressive but badly dilapidated manor house on the outskirts of the village. Although Britons with more money than sense buying a ruin in the area would normally not count as a remarkable event, the new owners are apparently immensely rich, and possibly of royal descent. The provenance of this information is impeccable, as it comes from our local postman, who heard it from a colleague who delivers the mail to the supercilious estate agent in Port Rabine, and who, according to Patrick, is on more than intimate terms with Mr Sourcil's exotic secretary.

To demonstrate the elevated status of the incomers, Madame Ghislaine shows me an elaborately embossed card summoning the whole village to a cocktail party at the old Lascelles *manoir*, which I see the buyers have already renamed The Grange. There is some puzzlement amongst my friends as to why anyone should want to call their new house a barn, but then, as Young Pierrot points out, upper-class and refined English people are known for their love of understatement. The new owners also have a hyphenated name, which, as a well-travelled man, he knows stands for much in England. In fact, he says, they have three surnames, which must count for even more. The card also has its own coat of arms, which must mean they are of the aristocracy, and perhaps even related to the Royal Family.

For a republic which happily cut the heads off its own supply of noble necks a couple of centuries ago, I have always found the French far more snobbish than our own supposedly class-ridden society, and even more so in rural areas. It is also a most curious paradox that so many snobbish Britons with a property in France go all out to socialise with and even ape local working people in a way they would never do at home. I often think how it would be if a pair of middle-class French urbanites bought a holiday cottage in Cornwall, then returned to show off their familiarity with westcountry *patois*, and boast about how they get on so famously with the man who comes to empty their septic tank. Personally, I think the French attitude to those with more money or social status than them is refreshingly honest, and nowhere near as hypocritical or confused as ours.

In our village, the thought of anyone with the remotest claim to a tinge of blue blood becoming occasional members of the community has given my fellow members huge pleasure. There will, of course, be other much more practical benefits now that a couple of foreigners with money to burn have taken on such a huge and badly neglected property.

Mr and Mrs Lascelle will be able to leave the draughty and permanently damp old building and buy a splendid new home with central heating, double-glazing and piping hot water at the turn of a tap. Although the new owners will be able to tell all their friends and anyone else in earshot all about their historic manor house in Normandy, the Lascelles will certainly consider that they have had by far the better end of the deal. The sheer scale of even basic repairs required at the *manoir* will mean well-paid work for local tradesmen for months to come, which will be good news for many families, and also for the weekly takings at the Bar Ghislaine.

What the Neville-Smith-Joneses probably do not realise is

that, though they may have bought a huge and once-stately home with three hundred acres of glorious Norman countryside for the price of a tiny terraced cottage in London, the true cost of restoring the property to anything like (or rather unlike) its former glory will increase their outlay by a factor of at least four. Especially if the rumour is true that my friend René Ribet, the Fox of Cotentin, has already been appointed as clerk of works to the project.

After apologising in advance for my absence from club meetings while away in Wales, I decide to try out my latest money-making scheme on the company. They listen with growing incredulity as I outline my proposals for creating a drinkable wine from a hedgerow plant, and furthermore, one which grows like a weed. Surprisingly, I find an ally in Old Pierrot, who takes the opportunity to deliver a long and rambling lecture about the history of brewing and wine-making in Northern Europe over the past nine centuries, and how he played a key part in educating medieval British palates.

According to his story, when he and William the Conqueror arrived in Britain in 1066, they found the natives subsisting on a diet consisting almost entirely of badly cooked vegetables and watery ale. Finding that the climate and poor soil made it impossible to grow decent grapes and the interminable storms in the Channel made it difficult to get a steady supply of good French wine, William had charged his *major domo* to come up with a substitute that would keep the troops from rioting over their miserable conditions. After much experimenting and consultations with a Welsh warlock called Merlin, the then young Pierrot had found that an infusion of lemons, sugar, elderflower heads, wine vinegar, water and certain other secret ingredients would result in a drink that made the best champagne taste like a cheap Italian sparkling wine. It was, he says in conclusion and as he wipes a tear from his eye while looking meaningfully from me to his empty glass, rather poignant that I should have come up with an idea which my old friend and fellow member had in fact invented more than nine hundred years ago. As I rise to get him a drink, our resident immortal whispers that he is sure he still has the original recipe, and would be happy to lend it to me if I promise not to reveal the exact nature of the secret ingredients.

Moving to the bar, I leave the table in near-uproar, and reflect how typical it is that my fellow members should have no problem in accepting Old Pierrot's account of being a contemporary of William the Conqueror and swapping recipes with a mythical magician, but are outraged at his claim that a wine superior to champagne could ever be created, and, far worse, created from English ingredients.

A little later, and my explanation to a baffled audience about the English habit of hyphenating two or more common surnames to make a much classier-sounding single one is interrupted by the arrival of a noisy crowd of unwelcome foreigners.

The outgoing mayor of Néhou has returned from his hunting trip to the Alsace, and arrived back in the village with a goodwill delegation. Unfortunately this ploy to win favour with the voters has backfired, as the group's stay has promoted little but ill-will. Rather than politely register their appreciation of this part of Normandy, the visitors have spent most of their time comparing our countryside, game, food, drink, weather and women unfavourably with what they are used to on home territory. Nobody in our club seemed to resent the slur on the attractiveness of local women, but the constantly disparaging comments about the availability of animals to kill and the quality of our regional dishes, drinks and climate has ruffled many feathers.

As the Alsatian group swagger into the bar for a pre-shooting *apéritif*, I see that they look no different from a typical hunting party anywhere in rural France. Although they are bound to be mostly rotten shots and probably too tipsy to draw a bead accurately on anything smaller than a passing hiker, they are all dressed as if for the invasion of a small country rather than a drunken stumble through the nearest woods.

Each wears the usual aggressive combination of ex-military clothing, ranging from the standard camouflage jerkin and trousers to a complete sniper's outfit, comprising mostly of a tin helmet bearing a forest of twigs, and a head-to-floor netting ensemble threaded with a mass of leaves and dead branches. Another and obviously more sensible member of the party wears a bullet-proof jacket, and most sport brightly coloured caps, helmets and hats which they must think make them look characterful, but which will certainly scare off any wildlife remotely within shooting distance.

In the armoury department, the band of hunters are equipped to take on anything up to the size and skin thickness of a rhinoceros, although they will probably be letting off their thunderous fusillades at nothing much bigger or life-threatening than a songbird.

Apart from the usual collection of shotguns of varying condition and gauge, one of the party is wearing what looks very much like a flamethrower on his back. This seems a little extreme, even for French hunters. Behind him, I see that a giant of a man has what appears to be a hand-held rocket launcher slung casually across his shoulder. On closer inspection, I suspect he is carrying it for show, as there are no missiles attached to the ammunition bandoliers criss-crossing his massive chest. As well as the most intimidating selection of hardware, the man has a huge and luxuriant moustache which shames anyone in our party, and puts even the Widow of Négreville's fine growth into the shade. He is obviously the pack leader, and though his companions are no lightweights, none matches him for height and girth. Pushing his way through the rest of the group, the man mountain lumbers away from the window, and full daylight is restored to the bar as he arrives at our table.

Without invitation, he sits down, oblivious of the

murmur of resentment from our members. As he hefts the tube from his shoulder and unscrews the top, I see that it is not in fact a rocket launcher, but a portable cocktail bar. From the tube, he carefully slides out a selection of liquor bottles, and places them on the table as if unveiling a rare and priceless collection of statuary. He then beckons to the man with the flame thrower, who joins him at our table, takes the container tank from his back, and opens it to reveal rows of bottled beer stacked on the shelving inside. Calling for an empty glass from a clearly outraged Madame Ghislaine, the giant hunter explains that he and his comrades like to take their favourite drinks with them, especially when they are in an area which is, to put it mildly, not renowned for the strength or quality of its produce.

A shocked silence falls as our members absorb the insult, then our club philosopher takes up the challenge. In a pleasant and conversational manner, he says that he has never visited the Alsace, but a region known to the rest of France solely as the breeding-place of ferocious-looking if cowardly dogs and a favourite dish consisting mainly of pickled cabbage must surely boast many other interesting attractions. Obviously unsure if his homeland is being insulted or praised, the giant looks at Jacques Délabré with a beetle-browed frown, thinks for a moment, then says that everyone must know that his region also brews the finest and strongest beer to be found in all France, if not the whole world. He has tried all the drinks that Normans make from apples, and found them wanting. He would wager that none of the members of our club would survive even a modest drinking session of strong Alsatian beer, especially the way he and his friends like to drink it, which is laced with the alcoholic liqueur, Picon.

After appearing to consider his remarks for a moment, Jacques nods and smiles, then says that their visitor has obviously not tried the home-brew version of Calvados, and which, he suspects, will make any concoction of Alsatian beer and fruit juice taste like a toddler's bedtime cordial. It just so happens, he adds, that he has a bottle of oak-matured and locally brewed *calva* in his saddlebag. If their visitors are willing to take on the challenge, he will gladly make a modest bet that our club champion can drink theirs under the table.

The challenge is immediately accepted, and the rules and procedures of the contest established. The visitors' champion will be the man mountain, and he will drink a tumbler of *calva* for every glass of Alsace beer and Picon that our chosen man can down. The first one to fall over will be the loser, and his supporters will pay for all the drinks consumed by both sides for the rest of the visitors' stay.

As the table is cleared and the Alsatian giant takes off his jacket, loosens his belt and smoothes his moustache in preparation for the contest, I look nervously around the table, already knowing exactly who will be nominated as the JBC champion. Although I have no great staying power, my rate of consumption is legendary in the area. I just hope that I can live up to my reputation and maintain the honour of the village and our whole region. For the first time I shall be drinking not, as my wife often sarcastically remarks, as if for England, but actually for Néhou and Normandy.

The word about the drinking contest has gone round the village, and more and more spectators crowd into the small bar as Madame Ghislaine strikes a psychological blow by appearing from the back room with a silver tray bearing my special pint mug. It has, as she demonstrates, a bicycle bell attached to the handle. She bought it for me partly as a joke, but also so I can summon her from the shop on the other side of the bead curtain when in urgent need of a top-up. The ploy works, as the dramatic appearance of their champion's favourite drinking vessel brings a ripple of applause from the home crowd. As I warm up by going through some elaborate elbow-bending and finger-flexing exercises with the empty tankard, a young boy is dispatched to fetch the bottle of moonshine apple brandy from Jacques Délabré's saddle bag. On his return, Madame Ghislaine brings a large tumbler to the table and pours out what must be at least a treble dose. Before she can screw the top back on the bottle, my opponent makes his opening gambit by staying her arm and insisting she fill the tumbler up so as to make it worth lifting to his mouth. Then, when it is brimful and even before our referee can fill my glass, he tosses it down his throat, smacks his lips and shrugs in disappointment. Our so-called special strength applejuice, he says, is even weaker than the official variety.

It is now time for me to catch up, so I opt for my party trick of drinking the pint of beer straight down while casually rolling a cigarette with my free hand. It is not a complete success, as I choke on the unexpectedly sweet taste of the Picon-laced beer, and drop the half-made cigarette. At this, the Alsatian monster laughs and says I will be able to smoke it later when I join it on the floor, then asks Madame Ghislaine for a refill...and a bigger glass.

Six pints later, and the *calva* bottle is almost empty, while I am barely able to keep my head off the table. The combination of strong Alsace beer and Picon is taking its toll, and I am in imminent danger of losing the bout, and with it the honour of our commune. Also lost will be the reputation the British have acquired in this country for, if little else, being able to drink beer faster and in more quantity than any other European race, excepting, of course, the Germans. I am also in danger of costing my friends and fellow club members a considerable amount of money, as Didier has been taking side bets on the outcome, and half the village seems to have had at least a flutter on me. Meanwhile, my opponent appears completely unaffected by the normally lethal amount of *calva* he has already consumed, and is toying with his moustache and calling for another bottle to be opened.

As I consider the desperate measure of calling a foul and accusing the Alsatian of cheating by soaking up most of the *calva* in his huge moustache rather than actually drinking it, I see Jacques Délabré go into a huddle with René Ribet. Jacques then calls an official time-out and announces that René will need to speed off on his moped and pick up another bottle of apple brandy, and suggests the contestants take the opportunity to empty our bladders at the *pissoir* outside. The giant says that he does not need to get rid of the tiny amount he has drunk so far, but will humour us, and may even make a quick visit to our rival bar at the village over the crossroads for a few drinks while he waits for the competition to restart. He gets up and lumbers off out of the door, followed closely by René, and as I try to get to my feet, I feel a hand on my shoulder. I look up and see my philosopher friend, who says he thinks it best if I stay at the table and do not expose myself to the danger of the night air making my condition worse. Although I do not see how I could feel any worse, I keep my seat, and am about to fumble on the floor for my half-rolled cigarette when a minor earthquake rattles the glasses on the shelving behind the bar.

I stay at the table as half the people in the bar rush out to see if the crumbling buttress on the church over the road has at last fallen down. A short time later, six grim-faced members of the Alsatian hunting party squeeze through the door, carrying between them the spreadeagled body of their champion. Other members from their group push several tables together to form a makeshift bier.

After taking the recumbent giant's pulse, rolling up one eyelid and bending to place an ear on his barrel-like chest, our referee announces gravely that the Alsace champion still lives, but is out cold. Obviously he says, the fresh air and famous delayed-action effect of the *calva* has combined to overcome their man. Reports from outside confirm that the giant hunter measured his length shortly after arriving at the *pissoir*, and completely wrote-off René Ribet's moped as he fell on it. It is a shame that it should all end so suddenly, says Jacques, but the contest is now clearly over. The Néhou and Normandy champion is still standing, or rather sitting, and is therefore obviously the clear winner of the event.

With extreme ill-grace, the surviving members of the hunting party settle the first tranche of their dues, including full compensation for the damage to René Ribet's moped, then stagger off into the night, carrying their fallen champion like warriors bearing a dead comrade from the field of battle. By now and with the pressure off, I am barely able to stand and accept the plaudits of the crowd, and create another local legend by actually refusing the celebratory drink I am offered by Madame Ghislaine.

Obviously incapable of driving home, I am helped to the door, stumbling as much as a result of the hearty claps of congratulations raining down on my back as from the effects of the drinking bout. Outside, the cold night air completes my downfall, but as I sag to my knees, I am still alert enough to register René kneeling in the shadows beside the remnants of his moped. Rather than assessing the damage, he appears to be screwing a length of heavy iron drainpipe from the *pissoir* back into its billet.

As the world turns turtle and I slip away into oblivion, my last conscious thought is to wonder if the piping was dislodged by my opponent on his way to the pavement, or if my friend the Fox may just have assisted the giant's crashing downfall.

The more one gets to know of men, the more one values dogs.

A. Toussenel, French writer, from *L'Esprit des Bêtes* (1847).

TWELVE

Last night we sat on the farmhouse balcony and watched an electric storm vent its passing fury on La Puce. As dark clouds swirled across a strangely glowing sky and crooked fingers of dazzling light probed the earth, I wondered if the dramatic events might be read as some sort of grim augury.

The ides of March are long behind us, but it would not take a fortune teller to predict stormy times ahead if I do not solve our spiralling financial crisis. I have still not got round to brewing the first batch of our elderflower wine, not a word more has been completed on the new book, and the continuing silence of our bank manager is, as bitter experience has taught me, an ominous rather than a heartening sign. Strangely, not a single potential buyer has arrived to view La Puce. When I phoned Mr Sourcil to say we would be away in Wales for the next week, I asked him about the lack of viewers, and he said that he had given details of our home to at least a dozen British couples. Perhaps, he suggested in only a half-jocular manner and as I heard his secretary giggling knowingly in the background, they had arrived, seen what the outside of the place looked like and not bothered to get out of the car.

Our ancient Volvo estate is ready for the long journey, and I have packed some local cheeses and French wines to take as gifts for the Welsh couple. Also on board are three old paint cans filled with my latest scheme for an unusual and hopefully lucrative income generator.

When he called last week, the collie-loving smallholder's husband told me he is a keen coarse fisherman. He also said his part of the country stands on shale, and the best bait is always in short supply. There has been what he called a worm famine in recent months, and prices have gone through the roof, with the going rate now a staggering £2.50 for twenty medium-sized specimens. Worms are as plentiful as field mice at La Puce, so for the past few days I have been deliberately encouraging our chickens to break into the vegetable patch and act as the poultry equivalent of truffle-pigs. It was quite a job to rescue the worms before they were swallowed whole, but I managed to salvage almost a hundred before Fred and Barney gave up in disgust. A small beginning, perhaps, but this will be a test run to see if, unlike some Burgundian wines, French worms travel well. And, of course, if they are to the taste of Welsh river fish.

If my scheme works, my new contact in Wales could become our regional agent, and there could soon be container loads of worms leaving the ferryport of Cherbourg on a daily basis, and our money worries would be over.

Our journey across the Channel has been delayed, and I fear for the health of our livestock cargo. Despite leaving La Puce in good time, we missed our ferry because of a three-hour blockage of the main road into Cherbourg. We joined the dual carriageway and ran into a huge tail-back, and naturally assumed it was the result of either the daily pile-up or the weekly roadblock by protestors.

It is the peak of the holiday season, so all groups with a

supposed grievance are doing their best to stop foreign tourists leaving or entering France. Last week, I called at the tourist information bureau in Cherbourg to pick up some leaflets, and found that the staff were all on strike. They were, the manager told me, trying to get their terms and conditions improved by blocking the ferryport entrance and putting off thousands of British holidaymakers from visiting France again.

Tuning to the local radio station, we found that one lane of our side of the dual carriageway had been closed due to a major chemical hazard alert. This, of course, had given every branch of the emergency forces a golden opportunity to swing into dramatic and completely over-the-top action. As we crawled past the bottleneck, a helicopter hovered overhead while a man in a high-visibility jacket leaned perilously out of the cabin and made completely unintelligible announcements on a loudspeaker. Dozens of figures in bio-hazard suits and masks were milling around three large drums by the side of the road, and a trio of gendarmes were standing by with machine pistols at the ready just in case of any funny business. Every vehicle with a flashing light in the region had obviously been drawn like a magnet to the scene, and as well as fire-engines, ambulances, police cars and breakdown trucks, I even spotted the driver of an ice cream van with its musical chime on full volume.

While we sat in the queue and listened to the radio, all sorts of experts were wheeled on to comment on the situation, and hazard a guess as to what the hazard might be. To begin with, the most popular speculation was that the drums had been hijacked from a cargo of potentially deadly nuclear waste on its way to the power station at La Hague. Perhaps, said one commentator, they had been placed there by a gang of international terrorists who wished to hold the country to ransom, or perhaps they had been dumped by activists from the farming union to highlight the danger of allowing potentially deadly British bacon, sausages and cheese into the country.

Just as the studio guests exhausted all the most extreme and unlikely possibilities, the programme was interrupted by a news flash, with the reporter at the scene interviewing the officer who was co-ordinating the operation. The official explained that the Arabic markings on the side of the drums had finally been deciphered, and it seemed the contents were a very strong acid. He was, however, happy to report that the drums had not been placed by the roadside deliberately, but had simply fallen off the back of a lorry. There was still an element of danger, but at least his men now knew what they were dealing with. When pressed to reveal the type of acid in the drums, he was hesitant to go into details, but eventually said that it was of the same sort of acid that is found in vinegar.

After a meaningful silence, the reporter asked if he actually meant that the contents of the drums were, in fact, vinegar. Following an even longer silence and speaking in a small voice, the chemical bio-hazard reaction task force co-ordinator said yes, they had been dealing with wine vinegar. But, he added defensively, it was a very strong vinegar. And it was not French vinegar.

Turning off the radio, we inched on past the epicentre of the emergency, and watched the glum-faced task force pack away their equipment and turn off their flashing lights, and the helicopter buzz somehow reluctantly away towards Cherbourg.

More delays at the ferry port as all outgoing vehicles are being stopped by customs officers, and their drivers questioned about where they are going. This is an unusual procedure, especially as it is raining quite heavily, which normally deters the most conscientious of officials from leaving their cubby holes. Also, I would have thought that the intended destination of people driving on to a scheduled ferryboat bound for England should be fairly obvious. Perhaps, in his embarrassment, the task force co-ordinator has forgotten to stand the port down from the vinegar drum alert.

In normal times, French customs officials are generally much more concerned with what you might be taking in to France, and seem only too glad to see the back of any illicit substances, stolen or dangerous goods, and especially illegal immigrants passing through on their way to the United Kingdom. Last year there was a much heightened level of activity around the exit gate from the ferryport, as the outbreak and spread of foot and mouth disease gave the authorities the chance to indulge their distrust and contempt for all British foodstuffs, and to impose some curious precautions. Some ferry companies handed out notes to all passengers as they boarded, warning that dairy products (including artificial creamers) must either be consumed or jettisoned overboard before disembarkation. The discovery of an old bacon sandwich in an English lorry driver's cab would probably have caused almost the level of over-reaction we had seen at the chemical hazard alert.

Before getting off the boats, all foot passengers were herded across squares of old carpet allegedly doused in disinfectant, and all incoming vehicles were diverted to pass through specially adapted carwash machines. Curiously, their drivers and passengers were left unmolested, and thus perfectly free to spread the disease by foot the moment they stepped out on to French territory.

The banning of such clearly innocent items as smoked and vacuum-packed bacon slices from Denmark caused much confusion and some misconceptions amongst would-be travellers to France. At the height of the crisis, I talked to a young woman who worked at the Cherbourg offices of one of the ferry operators, and she said she had received some very strange enquiries. A Scottish lady had called to ask if it were true that she would only be allowed to bring one pair of shoes into the country, and another to ask if there would be an embargo on the ashes of her pet dog, which she always took on holiday with her.

We have finally rolled across the linkspan and on to the boat, but not without incident. When the obviously irritable customs officer asked what we were carrying, I could not resist using the Oscar Wilde line about having nothing to declare but my genius, but it did not translate too well, and we were pulled over for a thorough search.

Eventually, a hugely fat gendarme opened one of the paint tins, and wanted to know why I was taking a consignment of nearly-dead worms out of the country. Thinking quickly, I explained that we were on our way to deepest Wales, and, along with bread made of seaweed, the Welsh considered worms a great table delicacy. Providing of course, they were prepared and cooked in the correct way. Obviously, French worms were the most edible of all, and greatly prized by all good Welsh cooks.

Rather stupidly, I had not seen the obvious outcome of telling a French gourmet about a challenging and exotic dish, so had to spend the next ten minutes inventing and writing down the instructions for cleaning, dressing and cooking that classic Welsh speciality, lightly fried earthworms in leek sauce. Such was his interest, I also felt bound to give the epicurean policeman one of the paint tins so he could try the recipe out at home. As he waved us through and on to the link span, he smiled, held up the tin and promised to let me know on our return how his first attempt at *vers aux poireaux* turned out.

Life can truly be stranger than fiction, or at least anything I could make up.

On the ferry, we found ourselves sitting opposite a pleasant young Breton carpenter. He told us he was going over to Portsmouth to continue working on restoring a house for a French couple. At first thinking he was mocking the way English tradesmen cross the channel to work on ruined French properties for British owners, I asked if he was pulling my leg, and when I had explained what that meant, he assured me he was telling the truth. Although the cost of the property had been hugely expensive by French standards, the couple were great fans of what they thought of as classic English architecture, and were sparing no expense in returning the house to its original turn-of-the-century condition. So far, the young man said, he had ripped out all the double-glazed windows and replaced them with wooden sashes, and was on his way to remove the central heating system. Next, he had been told to put a sledgehammer through the modern kitchen fittings and appliances, and install a butler's sink, reproduction zinc-topped draining board and a mangle.

I might think his story strange, he said, but then I might be surprised to know what some French people thought of the way so many English people spent so much money returning a perfectly sound and expensively modernised property in France to exactly what they imagined it used to be.

West Wales is very Welsh, but not, as far as I have seen, that much different from the Cotentin.

Our hosts' smallholding is very similar to La Puce, with a single-storey farmhouse by the roadside and sloping fields leading down to a small lake. According to Jack and Mary, it rains in this part of Wales almost as much as in our part of Normandy, and the mud seems to be of a very similar consistency. Like us, the couple keep free-range chickens and geese, but unlike us, at least try to do so at a profit. As they are English, they also know what it is like to live in a foreign land with its own sometimes apparently bizarre customs and attitudes.

Shortly after we arrived, it seemed we had been on a wasted journey. Over dinner, Jack broke the news that they (or rather his wife) could not bear to part with their new dog, especially now it has become part of the family.

As my wife consoled our sobbing hostess and said she would have felt just the same, Jack told me that there was another dog on offer. It was not a true collie, but, he believed, a pleasant and intelligent enough crossbreed. The dog, which was called Milly, belonged to a couple who farmed in the next valley. As they were lucky enough not to have foot and mouth visit their land, they had received no compensation from the government, and the collapse of the sheep market and death of their bed and breakfast sideline meant they had to declare themselves bankrupt. Next week, they would be moving from their farm to a one-bedroomed flat in Haverfordwest, and did not think it fair to take a working dog to such a place. Much as it will be a blow, they had decided to make a complete break with the past. A fortunate coincidence for us, he said, is that the collie-cross has had all the necessary injections to allow it to travel across the Channel, as before disaster struck, the couple were planning to take it with them on their first-ever trip to France. Ironically, they had planned to look at the idea of buying a farm in Normandy, where they had heard the land and property were much cheaper. Now, that venture would have to remain a dream, but Jack had told them there was a possibility we might be interested in their dog, and it pleased them to think she at least might be able to enjoy a new life in rural France.

After dinner, we went to meet Milly's owners. As we drove there, our smallholding friends said that nobody could have worked harder than the young couple, who had just been getting on their feet when the worst case of foot and mouth for more than thirty years arrived to wipe them out. Ironically, not because their farm suffered from the plague, but because it didn't.

As we arrived at the gate, a dog came bounding out to meet us, and my heart stood still, as she was so like Lucky. A cross collie-retriever with more than a hint of spaniel about her, she had the same sharp muzzle and big luminous eyes beneath floppy ears, a diamond-shaped patch of white on her deep chest, and a rich and glossy black coat. Just like Lucky, she also had a small pink patch above her nose, and beautifully curled and feathered wisps of fine hair sheathing her sturdy legs.

My wife reached out and squeezed my hand, and I had to turn away and pretend that the keen Welsh wind was making my eyes water. My father, who was a wise man in many ways, said that it was always a mistake to take on a dog of the same breed when you had lost a really special one. The new dog, he said, would never live up to your memories of its predecessor, and would instinctively know of your disappointment. That would not be fair to either of you. He may have been right, but having seen Milly, there was no way I could let logic get in the way.

While we waited for the owners to appear, the dog came cautiously towards us, then pushed her muzzle through the bars. Ignoring the others, she stared intently at me. After a while, I reached out, shut my eyes and felt the familiar wet roughness as she licked my hand.

From that moment on, Milly was my dog. But, as Donella reminded me in a whisper, the hardest part was now to come. Firstly, we must be approved as suitable new owners by her owners, and then, if we were, we would have to take her away from them.

As my wife had predicted, it was a difficult evening. Although they put on a brave face, it was obvious how unhappy Milly's owners were at the thought of losing her.

As usual when there are difficult things to discuss or do, I had suggested that we all go to the nearest pub. After an awkward hour talking about everything but why we were there, we returned to the car park and stood looking at each other, with Milly sitting quietly at her owner's feet. A big burly man with a full beard, he had tried to make light of what was about to happen, and had even made a joke about Milly being short-sighted. With a bit of luck, he said, she might not notice her change of masters. Even if she did, he said, she would probably forget him in a month.

When we had promised to keep in touch and I had said I would send regular photographs of Milly and let them know everything that she got up to at La Puce, the woman gave me a bowl and an unopened box of dog biscuits. They would have no use for them now, she said, and it would be a pity to waste them. Then, the man twisted Milly's lead around his hand as if he would break it, handed it across, and said in a gruff voice that I had best look after his girl or I would have him to deal with. We said goodbye, then walked across the car park with Milly trotting quietly beside us, and I looked back and saw them watching us. As I opened the door and Milly jumped in, the man looked up at the sky, put his arm briefly across his wife's shoulders, then turned and walked back into the pub on his own.

Next morning, we put my new dog in the car and said goodbye to our hosts. The husband was pleased with the tins of Norman worms, but I don't think there will be any commercial application. The worm famine is over, he said, and prices are back down to an almost acceptable level. In my original calculations, I had also forgotten to allow for the high cost of transportation from La Puce to Wales, which would have made the project non-viable, anyway. But there is some hope for another export opportunity. Our friend said he had been experimenting with the cheeses we gave him, and the local carp had shown a great fondness for nuggets of Camembert topped with his wife's home-made blackberry jam. Carp, he explained, are notoriously fussy bait-takers, and keen anglers will sit for hours trying to tempt them with all manner of strange titbits. Perhaps, he said, there could be a market for La Puce Luxury Carp Treats.

I promised to post him a selection of our most pungent local cheeses, and advised him to give his postman due warning. Our parting present from the Welsh couple was a very large bag of seaweed bread. So as not to cause offence, I said I would look forward to eating it as soon as we got home, but will probably give the package to the gourmet gendarme if he is on duty at Cherbourg ferryport when we arrive. Having introduced him to fried earthworms and leek sauce, it will be interesting to see what he makes of another unusual, but this time genuine, Welsh delicacy.

We have made a diversion from our route home to Normandy. As we are passing near London, I have persuaded my wife that we should stop off at a major French property exhibition taking place over the weekend. Our books will be on sale, and an impromptu signing session will hopefully help shift an increased number. I also have an ulterior motive, as tens of thousands of would-be buyers will be visiting the show, and I may be able to persuade one of the agencies to make a special feature of my photographs of La Puce. If that doesn't work, I can try slipping hand-made advertisements for the farmhouse into the books I sign.

While speeding along the M4, I even thought about staging an instant raffle at the show, with every buyer of one of my books getting a free ticket to win La Puce. After some calculations, I discarded the idea, having worked out that, not to make a disastrous loss on the deal, I would have to sign and sell more copies of our books in one weekend than have been bought around the world in more than a decade.

Two hours later, and we have completed the last mile of our journey from the motorway to the hotel. I like visiting London, not least because it reminds me of so many reasons why we choose to live in Normandy. When we make our yearly visit to the capital, an air of discontent seems increasingly to shroud the city. Walking down any street, every face we pass seems to be set in a rictus of either total self-absorption or suppressed anger. Most of the wearers will live in this great city by choice, and have a far better life and standard of living than any generation before them, but all seem frustrated and angry and obviously dissatisfied with what they have so far made of their lives. Nearly all will have profited materially from the obvious benefits of living in a modern urban society, but few seem to be aware of or to appreciate how relatively well-off they are. They are obviously missing something in their lives, but do not have the ability or time to work out what it is.

Having spent all of an hour becoming more and more depressed by what we see around us, we abandon our plans to visit the National Gallery, and retire to our hotel. As an ex-resident of London and now contented settler in our area said to me recently, it's nice to go to the circus now and then, but only a fool would want to live in one.

The crowds have gone, taking armfuls of property details and their dreams of a home in France with them, and we have had quite a profitable day. Apart from enjoying, as my wife says, posing as a real author while signing copies of our books, I have also met hundreds of people planning to buy a property somewhere in France. Many intend moving across the Channel permanently, and some much sooner than they had dared hope. The continuing spiral of house prices in Britain has meant that millions of people now have a considerable difference between what they owe on their homes and what they are worth. Some have enough equity to buy a modest home in France and live carefully off the balance.

During the day I heard some extraordinary stories, but none more so than that of a pleasant if slightly dazed middle-aged couple who stopped off at our stand to buy my latest book. They said they had moved down from Yorkshire in search of work fifteen years earlier. The husband had found a job as a dustman, and his wife as a chambermaid in a smart Kensington hotel. After looking for weeks for an affordable home to rent, they had reluctantly moved in to a council flat in a then quite seedy part of the east end of London. It was a far cry from their lovely tied cottage in the Dales, but better than living in bed-and-breakfast accommodation. Then, last month, a surprise letter had arrived on their doormat. Under a long-standing clause in their tenancy agreement, the council was offering them the freehold of their maisonette for the previously fixed price of £50,000. Checking out the local property values, they had learned that a similar former council flat across the road had just been sold to private buyers for a shade under £270,000. And, as they said, it had one less bedroom than their place, and no balcony.

Hardly able to believe what was happening, they had raised a bridging loan, and put their flat straight on the market. That morning, their agent had phoned and asked them if they would accept a bid of £300,000 if the buyer paid cash within the week.

Shortly after wandering into the property exhibition, they had realised that they would soon be able to afford to buy an idyllic cottage in France and retire, with never a dustbin to be lifted or a bed changed professionally again.

After congratulating the couple and resisting the urge to

try and sell them La Puce, I joined them at the bar for a celebratory drink. It is good to know that the madness of property prices in Britain does sometimes have a happy ending.

We have checked out of our hotel and are on our way to the ferry port, anxious to introduce Milly to her new home.

Despite its name, the Britannia obviously attracts a cosmopolitan clientele, and on the way down from our room we shared the lift with two Australians, a German family, an elderly French couple and a loud trio of Americans. When we stopped at the next floor, I made my usual joke about getting out so another three people could get in, and when the door opened we were faced by six smiling Japanese tourists with at least three suitcases each. Rather than step back and wait for a less-crowded lift, they piled in with enthusiasm and a great deal of nodding and bowing. As we set off again, one of them cheerfully apologised for poking me in the eye with his umbrella, then said that he was enjoying the ride as he caught the Tokyo subway every morning, and the crush was making him feel very much at home.

At the self-service breakfast bar, I noticed that the Japanese family were watching me curiously, and following me around the display of foods from all nations. They had obviously decided that they would eat what the natives like to break their fast with. I also saw that the Australians were helping themselves to slices of German sausage, while the Germans were piling their plates high with the full English breakfast. Unsurprisingly, the elderly French couple chose coffee and *croisssants.*

As the cluster of Japanese hung on my every action, I decided for once to take the healthy option, and loaded my plate with smoked mackerel. As my shadows lined up to do the same, I saw a dish of what looked like horseradish sauce, and put a dollop on the fish. After peering at the sauce, sniffing at it and talking to each other excitedly, the Japanese did the same.

Back at the table, it was not until I had tried my first mouthful of the sauce that I realised it was not horseradish. Looking up and seeing the Japanese party watching me intently and not wishing to lose face, I smiled and nodded encouragingly, and cleaned my plate.

As we left to pay our bill, I imagined a sophisticated dinner party taking place in Tokyo sometime in the near future, with the hosts inviting their guests to enjoy a typical and traditional English starter of smoked fish and banana-flavoured yoghurt.

Procrastination is the art of keeping up with yesterday.

Don Marquis, American poet and journalist (1878-1937).

THIRTEEN

We are safely back at La Puce. After all our journeying, it was reassuring to see the coastline of Normandy appear through the summer haze. Although I will never be more than a foreigner in France and love the country of my birth as well as anyone, each time we roll off the ferry and on to French soil it seems we have come home.

Leaving the boat, we stopped at the customs box to ask if the gourmet gendarme was on duty, as I had another Welsh delicacy for him to try. His colleague said that he had been off with a mystery stomach bug for the past week. It could not have been something he ate, he added, as sergeant Boucher was always most particular about what he put in his mouth.

As the long days grow almost imperceptibly shorter, our hard work throughout the summer has borne fruit, and La Puce has never looked better. The roadside hedges are almost neat, and the newly-cut verge alongside the road is laced with a pleasing mix of wild and cultivated flowers. Following its regular mowing by the light of a full moon, the grass in the orchard has remained obediently close to the ground, and even the elderly fruit trees have been severely pruned and shorn of their moss and mistletoe infestations. The track down to the mill cottage has been freshly gravelled, and the twee postbox has been repaired and repainted.

As the first breath of autumn approaches, we have been on regular foraging expeditions into the roadside copse, dissecting fallen trees to build up the woodpile to a reassuring mountain, and clear the way for what should be a bumper crop of mushrooms. At the bottom of the track, the mill cottage has been whitewashed to a dazzling lustre, the window frames and doors are as glossy-bright as Milly's coat, and the earthenware pigeon on the ridge of the red-tiled roof looks almost proud to be sitting atop such a pretty dwelling. Beyond the happy bubbling of the grotto cascade, the Lude runs free and fast again, in no small way thanks to Mr Trefle and his gold-panning activities, while the water meadow is aglow with a thousand *fleurs de lys* in full and golden bloom.

It is good to have a dog at my heels again. It is less than a week since we returned from Wales, but Milly has already settled in and taken her place in the complex pecking order at La Puce.

It will take us some time to get to know each other properly, but she is obviously already aware she is now a member of a matriarchal society, where any female is automatically superior to all males. As her former owner said, she is virtually all collie with just a dash of retriever, and the mixture is most evident when she bounds happily off to fetch a ball I have thrown, then refuses to bring it back.

Apart from trying to instil some respect for her master before my wife totally untrains her, I am also teaching Milly to understand French so she will feel at ease in her new country. When I try to persuade her to bring the ball back I am reminded why, when I first arrived in France, I assumed all dogs were named *ici*.

Experts tell us that dogs believe themselves to be of the same species as humans, and, if we get the training right, they will regard us as the pack leaders and do as we tell them. This is the same sort of progressive reasoning used by archaeologists, who spot a hole in the ground, then tell us in precise detail what the building they say was there three thousand years ago 'must have looked like'. Nobody really knows what goes through a dog's mind, but I have my own theory. I think they view us as a powerful but generally affable race of giant superbeings from the planet Neurotic, who are a total pushover if they (i.e. the dogs) get the training right.

A former working farm dog, Milly has shown no aggression towards and little interest in the chickens. She affects a casual disdain for Ermintrude, Blanche and Hen, but has taken strongly against the male members of the Campbell clan, and harries them whenever they appear. Donella believes this is because, as an intuitive female, she has identified them as rapists and bullies. But although she clearly has a brave heart, my new dog is also intelligent enough to avoid confrontation with any real source of danger. After an initial face-to-face meeting on the wooden bridge that ended with Milly leaping into the stream, she now defers totally to Cato, who tolerates her presence as long as the newcomer keeps out of her path and well clear of her favourite hunting grounds. Also strictly out of bounds is any chair in the cottage or farmhouse, the old sofa and mat in front of the woodburning stove, and our bed.

When she joined the household after spending years of living wild on our land, Cato immediately set about ingratiating herself with Donella, and amusing herself by leaping out of concealment and attacking me whenever I came within range. Over the years, and though still feared by postmen, poachers and passing cyclists, Cato seems to have mellowed, and since Milly's arrival she has almost gone out of her way to be pleasant to me. This would normally be a welcome change of character, but it is not a pleasant experience to wake in the morning and find a small present in the form of a headless mouse on the pillow. Anyone who has tried to persuade a wounded shrew to come out from beneath a wardrobe and be rescued also knows that this is not an enjoyable way to spend the small hours.

The weather has broken again and we have had the most spectacular of downpours, even for Lower Normandy. The day began normally enough, and in late afternoon we were working quietly on the vegetable patch when I looked up to see the chickens scurrying towards their quarters. As it is impossible to get them to go near the coop before the last trace of light has gone each evening, they obviously knew something we did not. At first I thought they had sensed a fox in the area, but then the wind dropped and an uneasy stillness fell. As we looked at the sky to see what was on its way, the light took on an intensity which would have sent any impressionist painter worth his salt running for his brushes. Then a searing flash was followed closely by a huge, rolling boom which echoed around the water meadow and set the delicate flag irises a-tremble.

Before the echoes had died away, the heavens opened, and we followed the chickens into their shelter. For three long hours we sat huddled in the coop, with the driving rods of water drumming on the roof and churning the earth to melted chocolate. The cascade swiftly became a boiling torrent, and through the half-open door we could see that the water meadow was fast becoming a lake. As the water reached above the wheels of the caravan beside the big pond, it occurred to me that a wooden hut under a row of trees was not the most sensible place to take shelter in a thunderstorm, but Donella refused to abandon the terrified chickens. Over the next two hours and as the tide moved slowly down the stepping stone path towards us, other refugees from the storm joined us in our increasingly crowded shelter.

And so night fell, with an almost grown-up man with philosophical pretensions sitting beside his wife in a hut which could at any moment become either a pile of smoking debris or a makeshift ark, trying to soothe the nerves of four frightened chickens, a dog, cat, grey goose and two ducks by telling them the story of Jack and the Beanstalk.

Until this morning I believed that Donella knew nothing of my plan to sell the farmhouse at La Puce. In fact, she has known about my scheme from the beginning, and has been working to her own agenda. I have not seen any potential buyers because my wife has been inviting them to call when she knew I would be safely out of the way, then frightening them off.

A call to the snooty estate agent at Port Rabine revealed that all the couples who have so far viewed La Puce have told him that they are no longer interested. Some said they liked the farmhouse very much, but had been put off by the mad woman owner, who seemed to relish telling them about the dry rot and rising damp that she said permeates the building. Other viewers were told that the road alongside our land is soon to become a motorway, that the farmhouse is subsiding and actually sliding down the slope on its way to the river, and that it is haunted by a whole variety of unhappy and very noisy human and animal phantoms. As Mr Sourcil remarked, he knew that people in England got up to all sorts of subtle tricks to help sell their houses. Some even filled the house with the bouquet of freshly brewed coffee to swing the balance, but it was the first time he had heard of a vendor actually encouraging potential buyers to breathe in the heady aroma of the blocked septic tank.

What is particularly galling is that I am now stymied by my wife's ruse. She knows that I know I cannot confront her, as I would then have to admit that I was trying to sell her home behind her back.

I think I may have discovered the cause of my writer's block. It is possible that I have gone native and developed the phobia which seems to afflict virtually every craftsman in our commune.

This morning a battered old Renault came bucketing down the track, bearing our reluctant carpenter and a bottle of his best home-brew. As on every other occasion I have seen Jean-Claude Goulot, he was wearing his blue overalls, but I knew this to be no indication that he was at last ready to start work on installing our french windows.

A general rule of thumb in our area is that the overall-wearing frequency of any craftsman is in inverse proportion to the amount of work he actually does in them. Jean-Claude is a classic example of this tradition, and I have it on good authority that nobody but Mrs Goulot has seen him out of his overalls, and then only at bed and bath times.

Having gone to pay his respects to the hole in the wall which has been waiting patiently for his attentions for nearly two years, my friend knocked politely on the door of my study, and suggested I might like to take a break. It was common knowledge in the village that I work too hard, he said, and a glass of his fifteen-year-old *calva* could only help lubricate my creative processes.

When we were settled on a sunny spot of the terrace, he poured a generous helping into two glasses, then carefully tipped a little from one to the other. This, he said, was not to ensure fair shares, but in honour of an ancient local ceremony which dissuaded rivals from poisoning each other during friendly drinking sessions.

Lifting the glass to my nose, I breathed in the delicate bouquet and realised that my friend had brought me a very special present indeed. Most so-called experts who have not tasted the pure and perfect result of the distillation of cider into farm *calva* believe it to be a rough-hewn and somehow inferior spirit, which does not stand comparison with a brandy such as Cognac. They obviously know little of how long, complex and artful is the process to transform a pile of apples into a bottle of golden sunshine.

For every litre of Calvados, a dozen of best cider must be sacrificed, and then only after maturing for exactly one year in an oak barrel. When the time and the *cidre* are ripe, the mobile distillery will arrive to begin the transmutation process. The owner of the farm must have a licence to produce apple brandy, and there is a limit to how much he may brew. This is why the distiller invariably arrives at night, when there is less chance of any over-production being observed and reported. If caught going beyond his quota, the farmer and distiller can face ruinous fines and even bankruptcy, or, as they say here, 'eating the farm'. This ultimate penalty is hardly a likely outcome, as the last time anyone in our region was prosecuted was just after World War II, and then, it is said, only because the producer tried to charge the local policeman for his bottle of illicit apple brandy. Personally, I think the real reason behind all the late-night activity and overblown subterfuge is that the participants love the drama.

When the still has done its work and the cider has been reduced to its golden essence, it will have lost most of its original volume, but have tentupled in strength. The more savage the boiling-off of the liquor, the stronger the resulting drink will be. A classic *calva* should, as the experts say, 'weigh' 65 degrees of pure alcohol. The longer it is kept in oaken barrels, the more flavour and colour it will gain, but the weaker the spirit will gradually become. Also to be taken into account must be the loss by natural evaporation of what is known as the 'angels share'. For the calva-producing connoisseur, it comes down to a personal choice of trading off quality against strength, but there are limits, and a weight of below 55 degrees would generally be regarded as unacceptable.

So, far from being merely some dark-of-night bootleg brandy operation, the creation of a crystal-clear, smooth and golden liquor of exactly the chosen strength and flavour is a masterclass in both technical precision and artistic interpretation. It is therefore quite fitting that the acknowledged masters of turning base apples into liquid gold are known as 'alchemists'.

But the art of making home-brew apple brandy is increasingly under threat. When Jean-Claude's father died, the licence to produce *calva* at the family farm passed automatically to his wife. But when Mrs Goulot dies, the licence will cease to exist. The ancient right to make some of the finest *calva* in Normandy will be denied to Jean-Claude, and the region will be poorer for it.

As we talked of nothing in particular, the shadows grew long across the terrace and the air sharper, highlighting the piquant bouquet and tang of the *calva*. After holding his glass up to the setting sun and looking critically and at the same time with some satisfaction at the results of his labours of fifteen autumns past, my friend suggested we take our drinks and look at the work in hand at the ruined end of the mill. He had, he said, been thinking a lot about the project, and how it seemed a shame to limit our imaginations to the fitting of the windows and the creation of a new mill wheel. Why not, he suggested, at least consider completely restoring the Mill of the Flea? He knew just how much my wife and I loved our little home, and he would be proud to help in returning it to what it once had been. Rather than the common stone used for every other building in the region, the new walls would be made of the finest hand-trimmed oak planking, and he would even create a spacious and fully-equipped cellar where we could one day create our very own *Calva de la Puce*. When he had completed his labours of love on the old building, the Mill of the Flea would be, quite simply, incomparable.

Overcome by the thought, I asked my friend to prepare an estimate, then suggested we retire to the mill to finish the bottle.

Although Jean-Claude's best price for the massive task would be far beyond our means for many years to come, I was not too worried about the prospect of taking on such a debt. As I have found so often in the past, talking a potential piece of work up from its original modest specification to a much grander scale is a favourite pastime of many rural craftsmen, especially when they have a glass in their hand. After my early years of frustration and now that I have become more used to the pace of life and progress in our adopted homeland, I can finally see the logic in and appeal of this way of thinking.

After all, if you are not going to do a job, you might as well not do a really big and profitable one.

I think I have had another good idea. Reading last week's *Telegraph*, I saw that a Gloucester farmer has turned a hobby into a very successful business by selling coloured eggs. His farm is about the same size as La Puce, and his forty thousand free-range chickens are descendants of a rare Chilean breed which lay eggs in a whole range of pastel colours. They have proved very popular, and the business now has a turnover of more than a million pounds.

Although we have only two hens and they have, as far as I know, no exotic ancestry, the newspaper article and my evening session with Jean-Claude Goulot has set my mind afire with the possibilities. It is well-known that the diet of any hen can influence the colour and (some people claim) the taste of an egg. Starting in a small way and without telling my wife, I could experiment by adding different dosages of beer, cider and even farm *calva* to Gert and Daisy's drinking tower, and see if their eggs develop a distinctive taste. If it works, we could invest in thousands of chickens, and set up a production line of free-range alcoholic eggs. Apart from cider and apple brandy flavourings, I could try feeding them on used brewers' grain and vinegar, and become famous as the inventor of the world's first ready-pickled eggs.

Just when I had motivated myself to overcome the writer's block and really set to work on the new book, the computer has broken down again. Donella is convinced that I have either been deliberately sabotaging the machine, or at best, am so inept that I keep pressing all the wrong buttons and sending it into an unresponsive sulk. Although I admit I am no expert on how to work the thing, I think there may be something less easily explained going on. Perhaps my subconscious reluctance to spend all day sitting in front of the computer has caused some sort of telepathic interference to the machinery. Perhaps the Fates have decided that there will be no more books about our life at the Mill of the Flea. It is even possible that La Puce is sited on the crossroads of some superhighway of mystic ley-lines which have thrown the internal mechanisms awry. Or perhaps it is just that the mice who regularly feast on the electricity cabling in the mill cottage have found a new home.

On route to Cherbourg and the computer accident and emergency shop this morning, I called in at the Flaming Curtains to meet Cameron's latest literary helpmate and bride-to-be. This week, his intended life partner is a doe-eyed Moroccan lady with a very suppliant manner, who speaks not a word of English or French. Another obstacle to her becoming Cameron's secretary and wife is that she is already married and has several children. As we sat on the terrace and did our best to communicate with sign language, Cameron introduced me to his fiancée's husband, and the mutual friend who had proposed the union. The matchmaker is called Serge, and is a tall and painfully thin young man with a shock of dyed blonde hair and a very pronounced nervous tic. He claims to be descended from a 15th-century Peruvian witch doctor, and also believes that aliens from a far distant galaxy communicate with him through his television set, even when it is not plugged in. According to him, they sent a message last week that it is in our world's interest that Cameron and the Moroccan lady should marry and produce a son who will lead humanity on to another spiritual plane. From what I could make out, the husband was quite happy with the proposed arrangement as long as he is kept supplied with cigarettes and *pastis* at regular intervals.

After the strange trio had disappeared to gather some special mushrooms from a sacred mountain that Serge says is located beyond the supermarket at La-Haye-du-Puits, the mood changed, and Cameron started to cry. He told me that he is not a fool, and that he did not really believe there is any future in his relationship with the Moroccan lady, or anyone else he has met. When he had taken another glass of beer, he said that he, like me, has not written a single word of his book, and is close to suicide. He has a wife and four lovely children in Aberdeen, and misses them terribly. Because of his drinking problem, he had not worked for more than a year before coming to Normandy, and there have been constant money problems at home. When his wife refused to come with him and try and make a fresh start in France, he had left her, and now sees no way of going home.

When I had sat with him a while, I promised I would write to his wife and ask if she would have him back, and left him sitting alone at the table, staring at his empty glass and quietly sobbing.

My computer has been resuscitated, and now I have no excuse for not getting on with the new book. But, as usual, the distractions at La Puce are many and persuasive. This morning I visited the grotto to seek inspiration, and found that most of the goldfish we rescued from the big pond have disappeared. All I could see of the hundreds we had carried to what we thought would be a place of safety was a pitifully small group, huddled together under the shadow of a large rock which was swept into the grotto during the recent deluge. If the power of the flooded stream could move the rock, it would obviously think little of flushing fish from the water basin. I shall have to go on an expedition upstream with a butterfly net and bucket and see if I can find and rescue them. If I meet Mr Trefle during the journey, I may be able to persuade him that I am actually looking for more gold deposits at La Puce, and get him started on clearing that part of our waterways.

Sitting by the cascade and thinking about my current money-making schemes, I decided I shall have to abandon my plans for the large scale production of alcoholic-flavoured eggs. After Donella had bedded the hens down last night and gone off to the big pond, I laced the water tower in the coop with a generous dose of low-grade farm *calva*. This morning, they tottered bleary-eyed out into the daylight, then turned savagely on Fred and Barney when the cocks tried to make their usual sexual advances. Now my wife believes someone is trying to poison Gert and Daisy, and I have been ordered to find, buy and rig up a sophisticated intruder alarm on the hen house.

Laughter would be bereaved if snobbery died.

Sir Peter Ustinov, actor, director and writer.

FOURTEEN

The hen house has been under attack again, but the damage has been caused by an attempted break-in rather than an escape bid.

While changing the chickens' bedding this morning, I discovered the beginnings of a sizeable hole in the wooden flooring under the feeding tower. At first I thought our chickens had been reading up on *The Great Escape* and had started on a concealed tunnel, but the positioning of the splinters indicated it was not an inside job. In any case, I doubt even our chickens could gnaw their way through an inch of solid planking.

Calling in at the Flaming Curtains this afternoon, I spoke to an old farmer who said the would-be intruder must be a rat. He told me they like to get at eggs as well as the chicken feed, and predictably added that the rats in our area are renowned for their size and ferocity, and have been known to kill fully grown hens, and even cocks. He has not met our chickens, especially when they are in drink and at their most aggressive, but I did not like the thought of losing my breakfast egg, so said I would nail a piece of oak boarding across the hole. He grunted sceptically and said that I must have money to burn, and, anyway, Cotentin rats would soon eat their way through the hardest wood. The only answer, he said, was to use a traditional poultry-farmers' trick. I should simply smash a bottle and mix the shards in with a stiff drop of cement, then stop the hole up. Then, when the rat returned and tried to eat its way through the new blockage, it would get a nasty surprise. Donella would never allow me to booby-trap the hen house in this way, but the farmer's solution shows that my scheme for giving the male Campbells a painful lesson by putting ground glass around the false vagina of a decoy duck was not such a fanciful idea.

While my wife is on ratwatch at La Puce, I have come to Néhou's first-ever cocktail party, and cannot remember such an eclectic gathering of local people, members of the region's *beau monde*, and British settlers. Our hosts appeared to have issued invitations to half the inhabitants of the Cotentin, and more than a hundred very assorted guests have turned up to meet the new lord and lady of the *manoir*.

Some will have attended out of politeness, and some out of natural curiosity, wishing to inspect a couple of foreigners who are mad and rich enough to buy a decrepit old farm building, then waste another fortune on making it a hugely expensive place to maintain and keep ready for their occasional visits. Some will have come to see and be seen, others simply to eat and drink as much as possible for free, while a number will clearly have more commercial reasons for their attendance.

In one corner of the hall, I see a gaggle of men in caps, boots and overalls, and realise that this is probably the first time in the long history of our area that so many local craftsmen have been seen together in the same place. It will be a particularly poignant sight for the groups of British owners dotted around the room, who remain desperately in need of the services of this abandonment of plumbers, roofers and plasterers. Some of the British women have no shame, and are quite openly nodding, smiling seductively and even winking at the group of elusive craftsmen, just like Parisienne streetwalkers on a quiet night.

Taking a glass of *Kir Royale* from what looks like a solid silver tray, I walk over to have a word with Jean-Claude Goulot. When I make a sarcastic remark about there being enough work for him not to do at the *manoir* to last a non-working lifetime, he protests that he has only come along out of respect for the new owners and to advise them on the best way to approach their restoration project. He is far too busy looking after all his existing customers to take on more, and thus risk letting any of them down. Despite what he says, I have a feeling he will not be able to resist the thought of adding the Neville-Smith-Joneses to his list, thereby increasing the tally of his non-customers by three names in one go.

Hearing a rumour circulating that even Mr Souder the plumber may be going to put in an appearance, I fight my way through the crowd to where an unaccountably empty space will give me a better viewing position, then realise why this area of the room is so clear. The solitary figure standing in the centre of the room and smiling hopefully at the distant crowd is Eric the Lonely. He is wearing his best overalls and boots, but the trademark bouquet of his profession still permeates the exclusion zone around him.

As I back away, I bump into someone, and turning to apologise, see that our hosts have a contender in the multi-surname stakes, and that not all the predators in the area are doing their business outside the old manor house this evening.

Nigel Teacher-Bell is a handsome and elegant man of late middle-age, with carefully distinguished silver wings of hair, an all-year-round tan, and a ready smile which exposes glittering and perfectly maintained teeth. He is as ever dressed immaculately in well-cut blazer, slacks and boating shoes, and will be on the lookout for any single British woman of uncertain age and certain fortune. According to Nigel, he is a distant relation to, as he almost apologetically puts it, both the whisky dynasties, and keeps a quayside apartment and motor yacht at Cherbourg for his regular visits to Normandy from his town house in London. As most of his past victims know to their cost, Nigel actually rents a room in a run-down hotel in the red light district, and the only regular sea cruises he goes on are the fortnightly trips across the Channel to pick up his unemployment benefit in England. We exchange meaningless pleasantries and shake hands, and I remember to count my fingers as I move on through the crowd.

Fighting my way outside and on to the terrace, I enjoy a breath of evening air and the fine views across the silage clamp and slurry pit to where the great *Val de Néhou* sits brooding in the twilight. When the rainy season comes, the plain will become one vast lake, but now cattle graze contentedly in the patchwork-quilt fields, and it is a most tranquil and bucolic scene.

As the single church bell begins its erratic tolling to signal the evening *angelus*, I feel a presence near me, and turn to see a tall figure climbing over the broken iron railings which run the length of the terrace. When he approaches, I see it is the amateur insect-hunter I met at Port Rabine. I also observe that his clothing is rumpled and muddy, and that he brings an odour with him that almost rivals Eric the Lonely's signature bouquet.

After we exchange greetings, he holds up a glass and explains that, as a keen entomologist, he could not resist the temptation of doing some field work while at the party. The ancient slurry pit contains a cornucopia of insect life, he says, which has thrived by being left undisturbed for many years. The small but fearsome-looking creature in the glass is a particularly rare specimen, usually only found in the rain forests of South America. Moving the glass closer to my face so that I may get a better view, he explains that the insect has a very short breeding cycle, a ferocious appetite, and can eat its way even through solid stone. Its bite can paralyse a fully-grown donkey, and the effects on humans can include severe diarrhoea, vomiting and even vivid hallucinations. He is obviously excited by his find, and says he intends to show it to the new owners of the *manoir*. With their permission, he could apply to have the yard designated as a place of special scientific interest, and they could even host seminars for entomologists from around the world.

I agree with him that it is an exciting find, but suggest he does not mention it to the Neville-Smith-Joneses until they have settled in, as they will have much else to think about at this time. Before leaving, I ask after his wife and her medical condition, and he absent-mindedly tells me that she had to leave the party after contracting a severe migraine. Apparently, she encountered Mr Sourcil the estate agent shortly after arriving, and his chosen combination of purple jacket, lime trousers and orange shirt triggered off an instant attack.

Back in the great hall, I hear a commotion by the bar, and see that, though the evening is yet young, René Ribet is already entertaining the guests with his Whirling Dervish routine. Going by his usual schedule, this will mean it will not be long before he does his additional party piece of a very long and earthy monologue with full accompanying hand signals about a milkmaid and a bull, delivered while standing on one leg and with a bottle of *calva* balanced on his head. As I walk across to join my fellow Jolly Boys Club members, I see that our local DJ, the Néhou Kid, is setting up his mobile turntables in front of the giant fireplace, and that the male and female folk singers from Coco's bar are already fighting for possession of the microphone. All in all, it looks as if we have an interesting evening in store.

The party is over, and I have returned to La Puce with a small bag which hopefully contains the solution to our current cashflow crisis. As promised, Old Pierrot has given me his ancient recipe for the elderflower wine he says he invented for William the Conqueror. The old leather purse also contains a number of particularly rare herbs and roots, of which the names, proportions and locations are known only to himself now that his co-creator, Merlin the Welsh wizard, has finally passed on. When I took a look inside the bag and pointed out that the allegedly centuries-old recipe was written on the back of a Rapido instant lottery ticket, he said that the exact ingredients and method were so secret they had never been written down, and he had carried them in his mind for centuries. When I thanked him, he said that I might also like to take note of the numbers circled on the ticket. They had been given to him by his old friend Nostradamus, who had accurately predicted the coming of the National Lottery, but died some centuries before it started, so had been unable to enter them in the draw. Pierrot had been using the numbers every week, but so far they had not come up.

Before leaving their party, I had paid my respects to our hosts, and found them to be more or less what I had expected. Both are raging snobs although they pretend the opposite, and clearly subscribe to that peculiar middle-class notion that everything about France is automatically better than anything in Britain. When confronted with such an irrational mindset, I tend to redress the balance by deliberately posing as a Little Englander. Unfortunately, and as my wife often points out, those who believe that the grass is literally greener in France than in England (though in Cotentin, it is, of course) are so incapable of detecting irony that they take me at my words.

Another - to me at any rate - curious attitude of our liberal chattering classes is that they find love of one's country admirable in the French, but despicable in the British. I can only think they do not know who Chauvin was or where he came from. After talking to the couple for no more than five minutes, I also believe they are not as truly liberal as they would wish to appear. The lady of the house may like to appear egalitarian, but I think she is the sort of person who, a couple of generations previously, would have been quite happy to work her serving maid to death while concernedly handing out charity parcels to the village poor.

When I advised her to get a firm estimate for any work our local workmen were not going to do on her new home, she looked at me as if I should be outside on car parking duty, then declared herself delighted that so many people from what she called the artisan community had turned up, and that she hoped they would be regular visitors from now on.

If it is true that the couple have appointed René Ribet as their clerk of works, and, as Madame Neville-Smith-Jones says, no expense is to be spared on the project, I have a feeling that our elusive craftsmen will break the rule of a working lifetime, and become very regular visitors indeed.

After watching the supermarket security guard hand out summary punishment to the young shoplifter last month, there came further evidence today of the cultural chasm between rural France and modern Britain when it comes to suitably disciplining their young.

At the dentist's surgery this morning for a check-up, I sat in the waiting room and watched a bored lad of about eight playing his parents up. An official warning in the form of a grunt having had no effect, the father casually reached out and delivered a whacking blow to the boy's leg with a hand almost the size of a small ham. After picking himself up, the lad limped over to sit very quietly beside his mother, who looked at him as if she was about to give him another *claque* for good measure.

On this evening's national news programme, the clearly

bemused presenter reported that a man from Beauvais had been prosecuted for chastising his son during a family holiday in Scotland. According to the report, the boy had been misbehaving in an Edinburgh restaurant, and the father had taken him outside and slapped his bottom. After horrified witnesses had reported what they called the vicious attack, the father was arrested and prosecuted. Admonishing the accused, the Edinburgh Sheriff had said that assault against children in Britain was a matter of grave concern, and that had he been British, she would have ordered the father to carry out community service.

The outraged Frenchman responded by saying he felt completely humiliated, that he intended putting in a complaint to the European Court, and was definitely going to write to President Chirac. As an ultimate act of gallic revenge, he was also going to change his favoured tipple from Scotch to Irish whiskey.

At the end of the bulletin, a child psychiatrist was asked to comment, and ended his remarks by observing rather dryly that at least the English might now be able to understand and appreciate why French children are so well behaved in restaurants.

Project Elderflower is at last under way. We have been hard at work all week making the first batch, and the floor of the mill cottage is lined with large demijohns filled to the brim with a gently bubbling, opaque and surprisingly pungent liquor. I hope that, when the mixture has matured, the wine will clear and take on a floral bouquet, rather than smelling worse than a pair of Eric The Lonely's favourite overalls.

Old Pierrot's recipe is very different from the one in my country brewing book, but as I said to Donella, this was only to be expected. If our local immortal is telling the truth, the taste of the wine that first touched the lips of William the

Conqueror will be unique. Whatever else, it will certainly be strong. When we made the basic brew and added the mystery ingredients in our period bathtub, the liquor not only removed the ingrained tidemark, but also brought the enamelling up like new.

It is now a race against time, and our future at La Puce is in the laps of the gods. Going through our accounts today, I estimate that, with no additional income and by living like hermits, we can just about survive till the end of the year. If the Elderflower Champagne is a success, it will help stave off the inevitable, but I fear that the only long-term solution will be to sell La Puce. We have not heard from our bank manager for almost a month, but I know that is not because he is unconcerned about the state of our account. Using an assumed identity, I called last week to find out if he was still there, and not been sent to the French banking system's equivalent of Siberia for his indulgences towards us. His secretary told me he was on holiday in the Auvergne, but had put a red-star reminder in his diary to call Mr East as soon as he returned. When I asked how she knew it was me, she said that, no matter how I tried to disguise my voice, no other customer spoke French quite like me.

Even after all these years, my wife still surprises me. During a long talk on the bench by the grotto today, Donella said it was high time we faced facts, and that we must accept the inevitable and make a real effort to sell La Puce and clear our debts. She admitted that she had been wrong to put potential buyers off with her horror stories, but I had been wrong in trying to deceive her by selling our home behind her back. I should also have learned after more than thirty years together that I was hopeless at trying to keep anything of any importance from her. What hurt her most was that I had not been more honest about our financial problems, though she knew I had been trying to protect her from the worry. We had survived before, and would get through yet another cash crisis somehow. It was not my fault that the world had yet to recognise my ability as a author. We both knew that I would be completely miserable if I gave up my writing and tried to find and work at a proper job. She had not stuck with me through thick and thin all this time to give up now. Once I had pulled myself together and got down to finishing the new book, she knew that the big breakthrough would come, and our money troubles would be, if not over, at least relieved. If keeping on trying to make a living as a creative writer meant that we had to sell La Puce, then so be it.

Finally, my wife reminded me of a speech Winston Churchill had made at the end of a prize-giving ceremony at his old school. When the pupils had settled down in expectation of a long oration from the great man on how to make their way in the world, he had risen, looked round, and said: 'Never give in. Never give in. *Never* give in', then sat down again. It seemed pretty good advice to her, she said, and we had always been fighters. As she gave me a hug and told me to blow my nose and straighten my shoulders, my wife said that she would rather live in a council flat in Cherbourg than give up on my dreams.

I know she meant everything she said, but I also know it will break her heart to leave the place of her heart. She was right to remind me about the virtues of keeping on keeping on, but it does not relieve my guilt about the hard times I have put her through while I have tried to make a living from creative writing.

As we went to put the chickens away for the evening, I remembered reading about a woman who had failed her driving test more than fifty times. Depending on your point of view, she was either being heroically determined by persevering, or totally unrealistic in refusing to accept she did not have what it took to achieve her ambition. Whichever is true, one thing is for certain. I love my wife more than ever, and I am the luckiest of men to have her by my side.

The first potential customers for La Puce have been and gone. When Mr Sourcil called to tell us they were on their way, my wife said that she thought it best that I showed them round, and that she needed to do some shopping. The couple arrived just as Donella set out up the track to the road, and she had to reverse down to let them in to the turning circle outside the mill cottage. After waving to the visitors, she drove off, giving me a reassuring smile and a thumbs-up signal. Walking over to meet the couple and try to persuade them that they should take my wife's home away, I felt as if I was being unfaithful to her.

In the event, I had no need to worry. When we had tramped around the ten acres of fields, ponds, streams, woodland and impassable scrub, the visitors went into a huddle by the grotto then told me that, lovely as it was, La Puce was not for them. Just by walking the land and hearing me talk about all of the advantages and some of the drawbacks of living in such a place, they had learned something about themselves.

For years, they had sat in their terraced house in Manchester and thought how wonderful it would be to live somewhere exactly like La Puce. In their minds and in the pub they had planned in exact detail how they would live a simple but rewarding life, close to nature and far away from the madding crowds of Salford. Just like us, they would keep chickens and grow their own vegetables, which they would sell at market. A keen DIY enthusiast, he would single-handedly restore any ruined or dishevelled buildings on the property, and they would get by with providing accommodation for visiting Britons, who would envy them their life in the heart of the French countryside.

Now they had put themselves in our position and seen and heard what work it would all be, they had changed their minds. Before driving to La Puce, they had seen a neat little cottage in a small village near the west coast. The property was as pretty as a picture, and it had been completely restored by the English owners. The gardens in front of and behind were large by their standards, but did not add up to the size of one corner of the wild patch of scrubland facing the mill cottage at La Puce.

There was also a butcher's shop, bakery and general store just around the corner in the square, and the property could be theirs for a tenth of what it would cost in the countryside outside Manchester. Having seen the wild acres of La Puce immediately after discussing what a nice flower bed they could make in the front garden of the cottage, they had been forced to confront and consider some realities about themselves and their pub fantasies.

As we shook hands and I told them I thought they had made exactly the right decision, the husband said how much they admired my wife and I for living out our and other peoples' dreams, and that they would always envy us. Perhaps when we decided to retire, they would be ready to move to France and make us an offer, then take up where we had left off at La Puce. For the coming years they still needed to continue their jobs in Manchester where he was a policeman and his wife a teacher. With what they both had to see and deal with every day, they often dreamed of escaping from the city and England itself, but it would be another decade before their children left home, and they would be able to take early retirement. But till then, they would be able to enjoy their little bolt-hole in Normandy.

Apologising for wasting my time, the man said they would go back to the estate agents at Port Rabine and put in an offer on the seaside cottage. If it was accepted, he hoped that we would come and see them when they were at their holiday home, and that they would be able to come and visit us, and perhaps help us work on our land while they pretended it was theirs.

I waved as they drove off up the track, then went in the cottage to start preparing a really special meal for my wife. Although our elderflower champagne will not be ready for some time, I knew there was a bottle of very good sparkling farm cider in the cupboard under the stairs. When she returns and sees what I have done, my wife will probably think that the couple have decided to buy La Puce. Then I will tell her that I have staged the celebrations because the nice couple from Manchester will not be making an offer, and that I just wanted to show her that I do know the true value of some very important things we share together, and that they are far more important than our temporary money problems.

The mystery of our disappearing goldfish may have been solved. After dinner this evening, we took our coffee on the bench by the grotto, sitting beneath a string of fairy lights I had rigged up as another little surprise for my wife. Looking contentedly down at the reflections dancing on the surface, I saw that there were now no more than a handful of Psycho's original tribe huddling around the big stone by the cascade. We have had no heavy downpours since the deluge, so I could not believe that the missing fish had been washed downstream. Then, a dark shape loomed up from the depths and the group scattered in terror. I could not see what it was that had attacked them, but it was far too big to be one of the mature trout that allegedly lurk at the bottom of our water basin. Something very nasty has obviously arrived in our grotto, and rather than moving the goldfish to a place of safety from the Campbell gang, it looks as if I have put them in even greater danger.

I have been doing some research on the Internet about unusual and large river fish in Northern France, and believe we may have the European equivalent of a giant piranha in the grotto. However, its arrival could be fortuitous. Searching the World Wide Web, I found a number of entries about a huge North European fish which eats flesh, and quite a lot of it at one sitting. According to the reports, the Wells catfish can grow up to three hundred pounds in weight, is extremely ferocious, and very, very ugly. It is said to look something like a giant tadpole, with bulbous eyes, and prominent, razor-sharp teeth. It knows no fear, and as well as having a taste for virtually all other fish, has been known to eat dogs and even attack small children. It likes to hunt at night, and the female can bear up to 300,000 eggs for every kilogram of body weight. Most interestingly of all, the giant freshwater catfish is much sought-after by specialist game fishermen, and can fetch £2000 on the black market.

I suppose it is wishful thinking, but if our intruder is one of these awesome creatures, there could be all sorts of benefits. If I could somehow make up a pair and persuade them to breed, our money problems would be over. Failing that, I could stage a competition for local anglers, with a hefty entry fee and a cash prize for whoever either hooks the fish, or survives the encounter.

Common sense is the best distributed commodity in the world, for every man is convinced he is well supplied with it.

René Descartes, French philosopher and mathematician (1596-1650).

FIFTEEN

What country people call the true summer is over, but the season of fetes and forgetfulness continues unabated. Sometimes it seems the whole of the region is *en fête.*

In the past month, we have attended festivals, exhibitions and general bacchanalias involving the celebration and sampling of cheese, mussels, sea slugs, oysters, pork, cider, beef, black pudding and even milk. Next weekend is the *grande finale,* with the St Anne fair taking over the town of Bricquebec for a very long weekend. According to the programme of events, the festivities begin on Friday evening and continue till Tuesday morning, but that does not allow for the rehearsal and run-down periods. Officially, the bars and restaurants and sideshows are supposed to take a breather between two and ten o'clock each morning, but over the years, the opening and closing times have overlapped until the event has become continuous.

To warm up for the St Anne, virtually all the other towns and villages and sometimes even hamlets in our region will have been staging their own wild weekends, each trying to outdo the other for dedicated application to eating and drinking. Many off-season visitors to the hinterland of the Cotentin peninsula must believe that the inhabitants are a reserved and even taciturn people, whose mood and sense of *joie de vivre* seems to match the prevailing climate. In my experience, nobody celebrates the going of the summer like the rural Cotentinese.

Perhaps it is their Viking heritage which is behind this manic final fling before the winter closes in. Whatever the reason, I believe some of our local people could teach their Norsemen ancestors a thing or two about staging a good old-fashioned pagan knees-up.

This weekend, it is our local town's turn to show its paces, and it is common knowledge that the St Sauveur *méchoui* is set to be the scene of an encounter between one of our area's most respected trenchermen, and no less a figure than the eating champion of all France. To add to the drama, one of the contestants will be representing our commune, and the other has been elected to eat for our rival village of St Jacques. This is sure to attract a huge crowd of supporters, and there is even talk that there will be a police presence to maintain order. Our local bobby attends every year as a matter of course, but this year it is said he will be wearing his uniform, which shows how seriously he is taking his responsibilities. Because of the renowned capacity of the two contestants and the increased numbers anticipated, a special supply chain is also to be set up so that the organisers will not risk the disgrace of running out of food. Normally, a comfortably adequate number of lambs would have been carefully bred, fattened and slaughtered for the barbecue. This year, I hear that the catering committee will cater for any shortfall by having a small flock of lambs grazing nearby, ready for instant conversion to really fresh meat if necessary.

We have arrived early at the football stadium to enjoy the preparations, and to be sure of claiming a seat in one of the rows of dining tents lining the pitch.

As Germans leave their towels on poolside sunbeds in the early hours, the tradition in our part of Normandy is to pay a visit early on the day or during the evening before an event of this type, and write the family name on one of the paper tablecloths in your chosen tent. Like most customs, this apparently quaint procedure actually serves a very practical purpose. Dinner-party hostesses and organisers of grand banquets elsewhere spend hours and sometimes days agonising over who should be sat next to whom to help things go smoothly and avoid potential embarrassment. Our simple method of letting people make their own choice of where and with whom they sit means that harmony and peace are almost guaranteed.

Whole tents are quietly reserved for some of the larger extended families, and possible confrontations avoided with a simple signature. If an individual arrives to sign on and sees that someone he doesn't like has already taken a nearby place, he will simply look elsewhere. Another interesting aspect of the system is that one can learn much about current disputes, family feuds and supposedly secret affairs just by walking through the tents before the meal and reading who has chosen to sit where. Friends sit together, illicit lovers make sure they are a respectable distance apart, and the tents colonised by the rival villages of Néhou and St Jacques de Néhou are always safely at opposite ends of the football pitch.

After signing on in the Néhou tent, we walk over to where the patron of the Flaming Curtains is setting up a temporary bar underneath the home goalposts. Alongside the bar, Coco's Land Rover has been transformed by some lengths of timber and old car headlights into a stage, and I am relieved to hear that, by popular demand, our local folk singer will not be putting in an appearance. He is to give his very first paid performance elsewhere today, and will be delivering his tales of death, disaster and perennial rural despondency at another *méchoui*, safely far away on the east coast. André Déprimé has sent his regrets to his fans, and promised to give them a special performance tomorrow to make up for his absence on the town's big day. Obviously, he has forgotten that the Flaming Curtains is traditionally closed on the day after the town's biggest outdoor event. Equally obviously, nobody has told him that the regulars at Coco's bar had a whip-round last weekend, and paid the organisers of the distant celebration to let him sing there.

Alongside the makeshift stage, a large inflatable paddling pool is being used as a giant drinks cooler, and hundreds of beer bottles float in an already melting sludge of ice. Amongst the bottles, I see that a number of bright yellow plastic ducks are bobbing incongruously. When I ask Coco if they are there for decoration, he explains that, when all the beer has been sold, the pool will become another fund-raising entertainment. Rather than fishing for the ducks in the normal way, contestants will shoot at them. As the inflatable pool is made of plastic and the competitors will be using one of Coco's collection of large-bore shotguns, the game will obviously not last long, he says, but it should be fun.

My friend fishes a bottle out of the pool and invites me to be his first customer of the day, and we sit on the bonnet of the Land Rover drinking in companionable silence. All along the touchlines, volunteer workers are putting the finishing touches to their stalls and stands, and I am pleased to see that, as well as the duck shoot, there will be the more usual traditional selection of games of skill and chance.

The nearest stall is a curious mixture of a fairground coconut shy and tin can alley, with some local refinements. The targets will be empty, non-returnable wine bottles, of which there will certainly be no shortage today, and in the place of wooden blocks or bean bags, the contestants will be using *pétanque* balls as missiles. Participants can roll or throw the heavy steel balls, with the objective of completely shattering one of the stacks of bottles at the end of the shy. The shards will be deposited in the nearby bottle bank, and the winners will be awarded a full bottle of wine and invited to empty it as quickly as possible so it can become a future target. Thus, money will be raised for local good causes, the customers will have a smashing time, and the glass will be ready for recycling before it leaves the sports field.

Next to the bottle-breaking stand is a rat-down-the-drainpipe game, where customers armed with sticks will try to whack the stuffed sock as it shoots out of the bottom of a piece of old drainage pipe. This is a particular favourite of the farming community, but it has lost some of its popularity since the organisers banned the involvement of live rats some years ago. This was not so much because of any objections by animal rights campaigners, but the lack of good quality rats. Had I thought of it, I could have invited the organisers to visit La Puce and try to snare the giant specimen that has been laying siege to our hen house.

As Coco and I share another beer, he tells me that he is worried about my friend, the mad *avocat* and would-be author and bigamist. He says that Cameron has been staying in his room all day and sending down for his drinks, and has not proposed marriage to anyone for more than a fortnight. He has not been seen skating around the church for weeks, and the proprietor of the Flaming Curtains fears that, as with so many temporary settlers in our area, reality and unhappiness have arrived with the dying of the summer.

I promise to visit Cameron tomorrow and see if I can cheer him up, then go in search of my wife, who is sure to be buying handfuls of tickets for the grand raffle, the first prize in which is an Alpine goat. It is bound to appeal to her, as the rumour going around the stadium is that the farmer who donated it only did so because the goat is afraid of heights, and will only eat the thistles at the bottom of his sloping fields.

Hearing an appreciative whistle from someone in the crowd, I turn and see the Jolly Boys Club of Néhou arriving in some style. First, a brand new tractor trundles into the car park, with Dodgy Didier at the wheel, and what looks like every member of our steering committee in an open trailer behind. The tractor is followed at a safe distance by a Range Rover which I know belongs to our new Lord and Lady of the *manoir*. Wearing what I bet will be the only beret on show today, Neville Neville-Smith-Jones is driving, while his wife is in the back, languidly waving at the spectators in a distinctly royal manner. The vehicles pull up, and Didier leaps down from the tractor and opens the door of the Range Rover with an exaggerated gesture. As Cynthia Neville-Smith-Jones steps out, I see that she has dressed for the occasion, and, in spite of the heat is wearing designer green Wellington boots, a voluminous smock dress gathered under her not-inconsiderable bosom, and a woolly shawl cast artfully across her shoulders. Having gathered herself together and looked around for some small children to be gracious to, she is followed out of the vehicle by four of our most elusive local craftsmen. They huddle protectively around her, and the party moves across to the bar, while Didier winks conspiratorially at me, then walks across to pat the bonnet of the tractor. Obviously, he has already begun providing the new owners of the *manoir* with the basic accessories for their new life in the countryside.

As the first batch of whole lambs is brought to sizzling perfection, a cavalcade of cars, mopeds and agricultural vehicles arrives. With all the seats in the tents claimed, many people will be eating *al fresco*, and it is obvious our feast is going to attract a record turnout. If I were one of the stand-by lambs in the field behind the catering arena, I would not be hopeful of returning home at the end of the day. Apart from the continuing hot weather and the need to get into practice for the forthcoming St Anne marathon, there is also clearly a keen interest in seeing who will walk away as winner of the official lamb-eating contest.

Joining my friends at the bar, I notice Patrick the Post is absent, and am told he has become the first human being in all Normandy (and perhaps all France) to contract foot and mouth disease. Didier explains that our postman was told by one of his customers, who is a retired British veterinary surgeon, about a slaughterman in England who developed the symptoms during the height of last year's crisis. The vet then made the further mistake of describing the symptoms, and saying that he had been involved in the outbreak thirty-odd years before.

The next day, Patrick was unable to rise from his bed, and is now complaining of a fever, sore throat and blisters on his hands and feet. Predictably, he now seems unsure of whether to be distraught at catching the disease from the veterinary, or delighted at holding what will be such a unique record. He has already asked Michel le Scabeuse to send the graphic details of his case to the medical journal in which Scabby Michael is regularly featured, and is talking about suing the British government for compensation for his pain and suffering. He has, however, sent a message through our club philosopher Jacques Délabré that, even though I am English, he does not blame me for his tragedy. He has also asked if, as an author, I might wish to ghost-write a book about this and other rare diseases he has picked up over the years, and perhaps even help him sell his shocking story to a British Sunday newspaper.

Now, all is ready for the *grand repas*, and by the time Kid Néhou has mounted the stage to ask people to form an orderly queue, the serving points are already under siege. Each family will have gone into well-rehearsed action, and each member will have his or her own responsibilities. Within minutes, plates piled high with great chunks of juicy lamb are being carried off to the dining tents by the adults, while children struggle behind them with dishes, pans and even buckets overflowing with chips and salad.

Then, amongst all this activity, an area round one of the serving points suddenly clears, and from it emerge the two main contenders for the eating contest. In the lead is the foreign champion, and behind him walks our local hero of the table, Alain Bourrer. Though well-made, both men are short and carry no excess weight, but, as everyone in our area knows, size is never an indication of capacity in these matters. Each is followed by a number of friends who will act as seconds, timekeepers and runners to and from the serving stations. As the two groups walk past, Alain sees me in the crowd, and smiles and nods reassuringly. He knows that I have a considerable amount of money riding on him, and that he, for once, is the underdog. Far beyond and above any monetary considerations, of course, he also carries the honour of our commune on his broad shoulders.

The parties reach the Néhou tent, and the St Jacques champion stops and beckons Alain and his team to enter first. It is not so much that he is being courteous, but he knows he is about to enter a lion's den, and will feel safer following the local man in. Lots were drawn to decide in which of the two rival tents the contest should take place, so we have the considerable advantage in that our man will be performing on home ground. We will need any edge this year, as Alain's rival brings a prodigious reputation with him. What was unknown before the match was made and the bets placed is that, apart from not being a member of their commune, the St Jacques representative is a professional eater.

Cashing in on the French fascination for physical oddities, the celebrated Monsieur Bouffe travels around France, taking on all-comers at official or privately arranged eating contests, and, according to his publicity material, has never lost a bout. He has worked his way through armies of *escargots* in the Dordogne, vats of *bouillabaise* in Marseille, and small mountains of *choucroute* in Alsace. Like the ultimate omnivore Monsieur Mangetout and the farting phenomenon

Joseph Pujol (more familiarly known to his fans as *Le Pêtomane*), Mr Bouffe is a legend in his own lifetime.

An hour later, and things do not look good for our man, or for my chances of winning the heavy bet I have made on him. While Alain has worked his way steadily through three giant helpings of roast lamb and chips, Mr Bouffe is already starting on his fourth, and shows no sign of easing off. The atmosphere inside the tent is as tense as it is stifling, and the crowd has long since finished or forgotten the contents of their own plates.

Apart from their consumption rates, both contenders are demonstrating their different techniques and overall stylistic differences. While the professional attacks his food with showy verve and seems to swallow almost without chewing, Alain Bourrer is a precise and methodical, almost finicky eater. Using the clasp knife that has been in the family for generations, he carefully slices modest pieces of meat from the bone and chews them steadily, lubricating his mouth and throat with regular sips of farm cider. In this game, he is the tortoise rather than a hare, and I just hope that he will have the staying power to win the race.

As Alain continues his steady progress, Mr Bouffe declares himself ready for another helping, and the bone on his plate is carefully scrutinised by the judges to ensure he has removed every scrap of meat. This is a vital aspect of the competition, and anyone who has seen a Frenchman working on a crab with a surgeon's array of pliers, chisels and needles will know just how fussy the judges will be. Wasting food comes way above picking one's nose in public in the Cotentin list of offensive behaviour.

With my throat dry from the tension, I leave the tent and go to fish one of the bottles out of the paddling pool before it becomes a shooting gallery. Sitting on the bonnet of Coco's

Land Rover, I see that, apart from the Neville-Smith-Joneses, a number of local settlers have put in an appearance.

Over at the bottle-breaking stall, our ageing gigolo Nigel Teacher-Bell is engaged in an animated conversation with a young woman who is carrying a large golfing umbrella. Nigel is using his shooting stick and one of the *pétanque* balls to demonstrate his swing, and is obviously aware that his companion is an enthusiast. According to her tale, she is a divorcee of independent means who spends most of her time improving her game at the course on the hill overlooking Cherbourg. According to some of the wives of our expatriate community, she is a golf groupie with a fetish which requires her to complete her personal best round by having sex in every one of the bunkers on the course, and is therefore known to the local caddies as the British Open.

The great eating competition is over, and the tortoise has beaten the hare.

When I arrived back in the Néhou tent, all was confusion as our supporters celebrated a momentous victory and the opposition sat in stunned silence. At the competitors' table, Alain Bourrer was unconcernedly picking his teeth with his clasp knife, while our local policeman was escorting an ashen-faced Mr Bouffe from the tent. As our champion rose to his feet and made the traditional signal that the meal and contest was at an end by ceremonially snapping the blade of his knife back into its handle, I learned from Jacques Délabré that the match had ended in a most dramatic and unexpected fashion. Rather than Mr Bouffe declaring himself full, he had suddenly refused to eat another mouthful, pushed his plate away and given best to his opponent. The losing contestant was being taken from the tent under police protection because the St Jacques supporters are convinced he had been paid to throw the match.

218

Waiting our turn to congratulate Alain and claim our winnings from Didier, I said to our club sage that either the fixing rumours were true, or it was simply that the legendary Mr Bouffe had met his match at last. After I had reminded him of the story of the tortoise and the hare, Jacques smiled, and reminded me that, as an aspirant philosopher, it was important that I understand that the explanation to any given event or situation is not always as obvious as it may at first seem. If, for example, one saw a young man and woman pushing a pram in which a baby is sitting, the natural conclusion would be that the pair are married or lovers, and the child is theirs. In fact, it could be that the man is the woman's brother or friend, and that the baby is his, hers, or someone else's.

While we shuffle to the head of the queue, my friend invites me to make an alternative construction to the outcome of the eating contest. Anyone who had taken the trouble to explore and discover any possible weaknesses in the armoury of Mr Bouffe would have learned that though (or perhaps simply *because*) he eats such a vast amount for a living, he is very fussy about what he puts in to his mouth, and where it comes from. He is, after all, a Frenchman. As further investigation would have revealed, Mr Bouffe is even more of a hypochondriac than our local postman.

If one were to think about it, it would be within the bounds of possibility that, though nobody saw it happen, one of Alain's support team, knowing of these twin weaknesses, could have waited for a suitable moment during the height of the contest before whispering in Mr Bouffe's ear. If that had happened, the whisperer could have told the champion about our postman's grave condition, and of the rumours that the lamb he, Mr Bouffe, was eating was not of local origin, but been supplied by Didier to the penny-pinching organisers at a very special price because of its English origin.

Given that this situation could have arisen, concluded our resident philosopher with a slight yet knowing smile, it would naturally lead to an entirely different conclusion as to why the eating champion of all France had suddenly refused to eat another mouthful, and thrown in the towel.

It is the day after the *méchoui* at St Sauveur, and according to the morning papers, most of France is in shock over a national scandal. It is not the news of the defeat of the eating champion of all France by a Norman countryman that has hit the headlines, but an even more dramatic story.

It appears that one of the country's most prestigious and savagely expensive wines has been counterfeited. The forgery has possibly been going on for years, and by far the worst aspect of the affair is that nobody noticed. Château Petrus is acknowledged as probably the finest Bordeaux red, and is priced on the menus of exclusive restaurants at up to £3000 a bottle. The scam was unveiled after a French dealer with a renowned palate bought two cases of Petrus, and drank some rather than selling it straight on. Now that truth has come out, special labels are being printed which can be electronically scanned to prove that the bottle contains the genuine article. The delicious irony is that nobody who has paid out a small fortune for a glass of Petrus in recent years will know if they rhapsodised over a wine which could have been picked up in any supermarket for a hundredth of the price they paid. Bearing in mind the level of snobbery exhibited by the French over both the quality of their wines and their ability to appreciate them, one thing is for sure.

Not a single soul amongst all those who suspect they have been rooked will ever dare to ask for their money back.

The troubled *château* in Bordeaux is not the only producer to have had problems with its wine. Impatient to speed up the process of our elderflower champagne last week,

I decanted one of the demijohns into a dozen old lemonade bottles, wired the corks down, and stored them at the back of my wife's potting shed. This morning, I found that more than half the bottles had exploded. As well as some minor structural damage caused by flying glass and the floor being covered by hundreds of insects obviously caught in the blast, the eruption of wine had drenched Donella's favourite gardening clothes. After checking that the coast was still clear, I hung the sodden sweater and trousers in the caravan by the big pond. With any luck, they will dry out before she needs them, and if not, I shall claim that I washed them as a little kindness, and that the overpowering smell results from a new superstrength biological washing powder on special offer at Super U.

The big pond is almost eerily quiet. The surface is like a tarnished mirror, and I could not see a single midge disturbing the still night air. Donella has gone to bed, and I am sitting with Milly at the caravan as I smoke a last cigarette, look at the stars and think about all that has happened in the short time we have been back at La Puce, and what took place in the two years we were away. My wife said she was having an early night because she could no longer stand the strange smell surrounding the caravan, but I know she knows it is a year to the day that my father died, and that I would like to be left alone with my thoughts.

Although I know he loved me in his own way, my father was often distant in his manner, and not given to displays of affection. The first time I can remember him letting me put my arms around him was when I had to tell him that my mother had died.

What they used to call a man's man, my father was brought up in the notorious Gorbals area of Glasgow, and though he rarely talked of his early life, it could not have been easy. His father had been killed in the early days of the Great War, and he had left school at fourteen to work and bring money into the house. Although he had little formal education, he could be one of the cleverest and wisest of men. I think he always regretted not having a proper education, and was scathing about people who had, but who in his view did not deserve or appreciate the privilege. His list of people without whom the world would be a better place included capitalists, academics, politicians, sociologists and all liberal thinkers. When we argued seriously, he would threaten to add me to the list. After one bitter disagreement, he did not speak to me for more than three years.

After his mother met and married an English sailor, the family moved down to Portsmouth and took a pub, and my father took on a number of unchallenging jobs. He was a big, handsome man with black hair and a wonderful tenor voice, and met my mother after he found modest fame in the city as the Singing Milkman. After being persuaded by his customers to enter a national competition, he won easily and was offered a contract to leave his round and tour the country with a leading dance band. He refused the chance of changing his life, and I think it was something else he always regretted.

When my mother died, we begged him to come and stay with us at our home in England if not at La Puce, but he refused. For more than a year he sat next to my mother's chair, determinedly alone with his memories of their life together, and he often said he could not wait to join her.

Although he was almost impossibly healthy for his age and the doctors could find nothing wrong with him, he began to lose weight steadily, and for such a big and tall man, became shockingly thin. Donella would cook for him, and every day I would buy him chocolate bars and small treats I knew he liked. We would sit with him at mealtimes to make sure he was eating, but still he lost weight. Eventually, he agreed to take some tests, and was moved around three hospitals and five wards in a month, but still they could find no sign of what was wrong. But

I knew what was happening, and that he was making his escape by force of will.

A month later and after I had visited him in the hospital, I was taken in to a side room and told that a shadow had been found on his lung. It had seemed to come from nowhere, the consultant said, and was spreading unusually rapidly. When I went back to the ward and told my father, he smiled for the first time since before my mother died.

He spent his last days in a Portsmouth nursing home, and during those short weeks we became closer than in the previous fifty years. He grew weaker everyday, but refused to go gently into what for him would be that welcoming good night.

On his first day at the home, he asked me to smuggle some drinks into his room, and threw a midnight party for the nurses. During the party, he told me the date and day he would be leaving us, and offered to bet me he would be right. At one time, he was a successful bookmaker at the local greyhound track, but gave me surprisingly good odds. He reminded me of his forecast every day, and said he did not mind that he would not be around to spend my stake.

Over the coming weeks, he became the staff's favourite patient, and would tell them dirty jokes and sing Irish love ballads to them in a still-sweet, clear and penetrating voice, which seemed more poignant coming from such a frail and wasted body. Once, when she was making his bed, he stole a kiss from a pretty young nurse, and when I apologised to her, she became almost angry that I had.

Towards the end, he insisted that I be the only one to carry him from the easy chair to his bed, and he liked me to put my hand on his forehead as he fell to sleep.

On the last day I sat by his bed and watched as he lay with eyes closed, talking quietly to himself, and sometimes to me. Towards the end, he made an effort to sit up, then lay back and held one arm out as if reaching for somebody or something. Then he smiled and nodded. I leaned over and kissed him on the cheek and whispered how much I loved him and that he would soon see mum again. Just before he slipped away, he squeezed my hand, and I like to think he heard what I said.

My father died just two hours before the dawn of the day he had said would be his last. I could not claim my winnings from our bet, but knew I had won something in our last few months together far more precious than any amount of money.

I saw old Autumn in the misty morn
Stand shadowless like Silence, listening
To silence.

Thomas Hood, English poet and humourist (1799-1845).

SIXTEEN

The mellow, mist-full days and glorious shades of gold along Hunters Walk put me in mind of a classic English autumn, and will be a most fitting backdrop for our cricket match at La Puce.

According to my brewing book, our first bottling of elderflower champagne-style sparkling wine will not be in peak condition until after Christmas, but our financial situation is pressing, and I need some advance orders. Following the accident in the potting shed, I took care to decant the remainder of the first batch into proper champagne bottles, and to use extra-strong wire caps to keep the corks in. The bottles were very expensive as they are always in great demand from home-brew *calva* makers, but so far there have been no explosions, and the bottling has also cured the problem of the distinctive odour which has been pervading the mill for weeks.

To publicise the forthcoming availability of our new wine in good time for the Christmas market, we are to stage a buffet reception and tasting at La Puce. To avoid causing offence by acknowledging that our champagne is not intended as a real challenge to the existing French varieties, I plan to emphasise its very Englishness by holding a friendly cricket match before the tasting.

After all the derogatory remarks and jibes about the state of British sport from members of the Jolly Boys Club, I have taken revenge by challenging them to field a side against my All-England Invitation XI. Buoyed up and over-confident because of their country's recent successes in international rugby and football competitions, the JBC sports committee accepted on the spot. As Old Pierrot reminded me in his official acceptance speech, the idea for cricket was stolen from Norman pikemen during the Battle of Agincourt anyway, so the necessary skills to excel at the modern game will be, like every Frenchman's natural ability in cooking and love-making, in their genes.

My next task was to recruit a crack side to play for the honour of our home country, and it was not as easy as I thought. After calling and visiting every British male in the area with the necessary complement of arms and legs and the basic ability to use them, I could only dredge up half a dozen volunteers, so have had to resort to bribing some of the members of our settlers' club with promises of free cases of our new wine if they turn up on the big day. On paper, we now have a team of sorts, but it is as short on talent as it is long on unusual characters.

Cameron has been persuaded to keep wicket, and dissuaded from wearing his rollerblades during the match. He has also promised to stay sober until after stumps are drawn, or at least until the tea interval. I know that Nigel Teacher-Bell will make a useful opening batsman to partner me, and he claims to be a former Oxford Blue. In fact, it is alleged locally he gained his skills by playing for the Maidstone Prison 'A' side during a spell he served there for obtaining money by false pretences. As the youngest member of the team, Bob The Builder will head up our pace attack, and has said he will bring some second-hand cricket kit with him during his next smuggling trip across the Channel. The architect who has difficulty distinguishing left from right will serve as a lower order batsman and bowler, and I am hoping his constant changing of stance and delivery will help confuse the opposing side. The husband of the Jerry Hall lookalike and the defrocked priest have also promised to take part, and I am hoping to teach Anton the former hand actor to make use of his considerable dexterity to deliver some demon googlies. I have also managed to get the entomologist from Port Rabine to play by telling him he is sure to find some very interesting specimens to study while on-duty in the outfield. The man who is obsessively restoring his farmhouse outside the village has said he will try to find the time to attend, but I have put him down as twelfth man as I don't think he will show. The breeder of mutant cockerels has said he will act as our physiotherapist, and his wife will help Donella make the sandwiches for the tea interval.

In desperation, I have also invited our self-appointed Lord of the Néhou *manoir* to make up the number. When I called, his wife answered and said they were very busy with restoration work, but as most of the local craftsmen working on the house would apparently be playing in the match, she and her husband would be pleased to attend. When I asked her how the work was progressing, she confessed that it was all taking a little longer and costing rather more than they had expected. There was also a problem with some of the ancient doorways having to be filled in and new entrances and exits made, as the *feng-shui* consultant she called in from Paris said they were in bad alignment, and would let all the luck out of the property if left where they were. It was unfortunate, she said, but had to be done if they were going to restore the old manor house sympathetically while ensuring that good fortune dwelled within. When I told my wife about the conversation, she said that, rather than the old Lascelles house, it will be the Neville-Smith-Jones who will need most of the sympathy and all of the luck.

After a long day, the cricket pitch is ready. It looks rather unconventional, as the field and pitch slope steeply down from the road to the water meadow. At least bowlers at either end will be equally advantaged or handicapped by the drop of around six feet between the two sets of wickets.

There will also be a problem with our moles, as they have already started work on the area of newly-mown grass. Before coming to La Puce, I used to think that my gardening friends made too much of a fuss about a few bumps on their lawns, but over our years here, I have learned why such small creatures arouse such large passions. Although I have never seen one, our variety must be as big as fully-grown cats, and as contrary as they are hyperactive. There are acres of waste land at La Puce where they could go about their business without troubling us, but always insist on raising their gigantic mounds in the middle of a pathway, or even beneath paving slabs. When Donella laid the terrace outside the mill cottage, they actually tried to force their way through four inches of solid concrete. The piles of tunnel dirt are huge, and I am sure they are deliberately trying to make mountains out of their molehills. Perhaps it is a status thing, and the males are competing with each other to make the biggest hill, or perhaps the reason the pathway from the mill cottage to the big pond looks like an SAS assault course is the old country conviction that moles are attracted to the sound of footsteps. Last year we tried out the theory by creeping softly along the path for a week, but the only result was a range of even more gigantic eruptions, and two ruined pairs of bedroom slippers. For the cricket match, however, I hope I can turn the phenomenon to our advantage. If I can fiddle the toss and put our side in first, by the time our opponents come out to play, the batting crease should resemble a scale model of the Himalayas, and be a perfect surface on which to pitch my special leg-break Chinaman deliveries.

Unfortunately, our grotto has not become home to a rare, valuable and ferocious giant Wells catfish. Last evening I got another glimpse of the creature that has been lurking at the bottom of the water basin, and I saw that it is a very large freshwater eel. Apart from the disappointment that I will not be able to sacrifice any poachers by feeding them to a flesh-eating predator, it is fascinating to think that our new resident has arrived at the end of a three-year, four-thousand-mile journey. Freshwater eels in Europe can grow up to fifty inches long, and once again, La Puce seems to have exerted its mystical attraction to particularly large examples of any species.

If it survives to reach the age of ten, our giant eel will make the return journey to spawn, and then die having played its part in the everlasting cycle of procreation.

In the meantime, I can take advantage of the huge size and menacing appearance of this fascinating creature by starting a rumour that the mad Englishman at La Puce has introduced a baby anaconda in his water basin which, when grown to full size, will be ready to leap up and wrap its body around trespassers, then crush and swallow them whole.

There has been a bloody punch-up at the hen house, and the pecking order has changed. In the past month, the smaller of our two bantam cocks has been becoming more and more flagrant in his couplings with Daisy, and has even taken to leaping on her in full view of her husband. This afternoon I saw Barney hiding behind the water-butt outside the mill cottage, and as Fred strutted past followed dutifully by the two hens, he leapt out and upon Daisy. It was all over in seconds, and Fred seemed too shocked to react.

In the normal routine, the two hens and Fred make their way to the coop at dusk, while Barney retires grudgingly to his bachelor quarters, but this evening, I heard a tremendous squawking coming from behind the mill cottage, and thinking that a fox had got in, ran to the coop. It was swaying from side to side like a dinghy in a rough sea, and when I opened the door, I saw Fred and Barney were engaged in a furious fight, while the hens looked on unconcernedly from the top perch. I managed to separate the fighting cocks at the cost of a badly pecked finger, and Fred staggered out with blood streaming from his torn comb. As Barney came to the door of the hut and let out a victorious crow, Fred stood his ground for a moment, then backed off, let out a pitiful squeak, and finally flapped up to sit miserably on the roof.

I came back after dark to find Barney standing smugly between the two hens in the coop, and Fred in the hut that had been his rival's former home. I went in and sat with him for an hour and tried to cheer him up, explaining how fickle females can be, and that he must accept his new situation. Then, I went back to the mill cottage thinking how, despite my wife's best attempts to impose civilised standards on her menagerie, nature will invariably have its way.

Dawn is reaching across the water meadow with saffron-stained fingers, and a gentle breeze from the west brings an occasional Mexican wave from the waist-high grass on the far side of the big pond. We have been on an eel-spotting vigil at the grotto, but there has been no sign of our new guest. He is obviously a shy creature, and my wife believes he is a figment of my imagination. She has decided to call him Elvis, as she believes my sighting to be as reliable as those of all the people who claim to have seen the late superstar in their local supermarket or chip shop.

Most noticeable by their absence during our time at the water basin were the hordes of midges that usually line up to feast on my wife at any time of day or night. I suggested that it might be the lurking presence of the eel that had frightened them off, but she thinks it more likely to be the dreadful reek coming from her clothes after their drenching in immature elderflower wine.

Later in the day, and while creeping up Hunters Walk to try and catch a glimpse of Elvis, I saw a glint in a patch of bracken, reached in and pulled out a golden egg. I knew it could not be made of real gold, as it was far too light, but thought for a moment the emotional disturbance in the hen house may have caused Gert or Daisy to quite literally go off-colour. Knowing the premium price that unusually coloured eggs are reaching in England, I wondered if the punch-up between Fred and Barney might have presented us with a golden opportunity. As I sat thinking of the possibilities, I heard a harsh snort of vindictive amusement, and saw Mr Trefle watching me from behind the Hobbit tree. He has obviously worked out my ploy to get him to clear the waters of our stream, and was getting his own back in a very childish way.

After congratulating him on his little joke, I told him that the real reason I wanted the water in the Lude to run more swiftly was to provide more oxygen for my new water boa. When I had described the size to which it would grow, how it could swallow men whole and that the word *anaconda* is Tamil for elephant-killer, I invited him to come to the grotto and help me feed it with a dead sheep. He refused, and after promising not to tell anyone, made his excuses and left. As well as a nosey neighbour, Mr Trefle is a notorious gossip, so I expect to see a noticeable drop in visiting anglers who believe it their natural right to fish in my waters.

Patrick the Post is out of his self-imposed quarantine, and arrived this morning with our backlog of mail and yet another medical complaint. After he had taken me through all the stages of his suffering and gradual recovery, he said that he was now intending to sue not only the British government, but also his own doctor, who had the nerve to tell him that he had not caught foot and mouth disease. His diagnosis that the blisters on Patrick's feet were caused by his shoes being at least a size too big, and his sore throat was a natural result of smoking at least a hundred cigarettes a day was not only risible, but grossly offensive. So upset had he been by the encounter with what he called our local quack, that he has now developed an obsessive aversion to the medical profession as a whole. The paradoxical situation he finds himself in now is that, because of the particular nature of his allergy, he will not be able to bring himself to visit the doctor to have it treated.

Our postman has left to continue delivering his letters and tale of woe to the rest of his customers, and we have settled down on the terrace to enjoy breakfast while reading our mail. Going by the pile of envelopes on the table, I shall be kept busy for days replying to the letters from friends and readers in other parts of France and around the world, and that will give me another excuse for avoiding getting on with the new book.

The first letter I read out aloud is from old friends who are having a challenging time in Gascony. They are a hard-working, resourceful and indefatigable couple, which is just as well, given their experiences at the hands of the Fates. They have tried more schemes for survival in France than we have, and been even more unsuccessful with most of them. The difference is that their misfortunes have not been of their own making.

Jean and Terry used to run two very successful public houses in Surrey, but woke up one morning to find that the manager of one pub had disappeared with the head barmaid at the other. He had also taken the week's cash takings at both pubs with him, and left behind a huge debt for drinks he had ordered on credit, then sold on at a good price to the rival pub down the road.

Selling up and moving to live in their holiday home in France, the couple had decided, understandably, that they had had enough of a life behind bars, and looked round for some other way they could earn a reasonable living dealing in cash and without having to employ staff. Seeing the rising number of English settlers in their region, they decided to start a market stall specialising in British foodstuffs. For two years, Terry would make a weekly return journey of more than a thousand miles, raiding Hampshire supermarkets for the sort of products he knew would be popular with British buyers but were unavailable in France. After building up a thriving business, the couple were put out of business by the French supermarkets, who saw the popularity of the couple's lines, and started selling them at a cheaper price than Terry and Jean could buy for.

Their next good idea came when they saw how many British buyers were in need of earth to be moved around to make room for new foundations, waste and water pipes, electrical cables, septic tanks and swimming pools, and how few were the farmers with really suitable diggers to do the work. Borrowing the money from the anglophile manager of a local bank, Terry went to England, bought a second-hand JCB, and had it shipped to France. With a number of jobs already in the pipeline, the enormously expensive earthmover was stolen along with the lorry carrying it, and on the day before the insurance came into effect.

In their letter, our friends have written to say that they are still undeterred by the mischievous gods' little game with their lives, and have started a business restoring old properties for British buyers who do not want the problem of organising or doing the work themselves. The business is going well, but they have had a slight setback with their latest contract. With a new extension nearing completion and ready for the roof, the job of the day was to hoist and fix in place a long oak beam to connect the former end wall of the house to the new one. Needing help to get the massive beam trimmed, cut and lifted, the couple had called in local labour. They had, as Terry says, thought it safe to leave the cutting of the beam to the precise length to the town hairdresser, and he had set to with a will and his own chainsaw. Unfortunately, there had been a breakdown in communications over the amount to be cut off, and the hairdresser had snipped off three metres instead of just one.

Now, our friends have the choice of buying another expensive beam, for which they do not have the money, or taking the new end wall of the building down and rebuilding it closer to the original one. To add insult to injury, Terry says he dropped in for a trim at the hairdresser's salon the following week, and not only did the man charge him, but also cut off much more than his customer had asked for.

Our next letter comes from a couple who write to tell us they have started a new drinks fashion in the Corrèze department. Before moving over, they went on a charm offensive by giving miniature bottles of whisky to every man in their hamlet, and bottles of lavender toilet water to their wives. Some weeks later and after a long day moving in to their new home, they decided to visit the nearest bar to celebrate, and were intrigued to see a notice advertising *whisky à l'anglaise*. When they asked about it, the barman said he had introduced the drink in their honour, as several of their neighbours had commented on how well their Scotch and special mixing water went together in the hitherto unknown English drink.

Next is a somewhat brusque note from a former schoolteacher, recently settled in the Dordogne. From what she says, the plumbers in her area are as elusive as our Mr Souder, and just as eccentric, leading to a messy problem with her washing machine. The drainage tube had been connected to the waste pipes from her bathroom, and when she flushes the toilet, what she calls waste matter is propelled into the drum of the machine at great velocity. This, she says, is not at all convenient, especially when the device is loaded with the week's wash. Even if she could find the plumber responsible for the problem, she does not speak a word of French. She has no husband, and all the British men in the area are even more useless and unreliable than I seem to be, so she is prepared to make me an offer. If I will come down and sort out her plumbing, she will give me free accommodation overnight, and even buy another of my books.

I shall write to the lady and try to help solve her problems, with my first suggestion being that she should avoid using or at least flushing her toilet when her machine is loaded with the weekly wash. I say to my wife that the woman is being unreasonable in expecting me to travel a thousand miles to reroute her soil pipes. Donella replies that I should be flattered that, having read one of our books, the lady thinks I am capable of doing the job, and, anyway, she would like to bet Peter Mayle or Bill Bryson don't get this sort of fan mail.

I have taken a break from answering our correspondence to attend an Extraordinary General Meeting of the Jolly Boys Club. I also meant to ask Old Pierrot if our elderflower wine will be ripe for drinking at the launch next week, and was surprised to hear he is ill. According to one of the members, he sent a message by one of his carrier ravens to make his apologies, and to say he is sad to have to miss a club meeting for the first time since the JBC was formed (which he claims to have been shortly after Wellington's misreported victory at Waterloo).

I arrived to find my fellow members in a great state of excitement, as it now appears we have definitive proof that our region's fine brandy should be called Cotentin, not Calvados.

The indisputable evidence has been unearthed by a scholar studying the legacy of the Sire de Gouberville, who was the author of a set of fascinating diaries generally accepted as being the oldest and most comprehensive record of rural life in Europe. In the way of these things, the Sire did not live in Gouberville, which is a village to the east of the peninsula, but in a manor house no more than twenty miles from Néhou as one of Old Pierrot's ravens flies. The astounding news is that a re-translation of one of the entries shows that in the March of 1553, the Sire received a young man from Touraine, who showed him how to make brandy from wine. Gouberville further records that, having made a first, botched attempt, he called in a local artisan to make a special boiler, and then set about continuing his experiments with fruits from his own farm.

So, after centuries of heated debate, it appears beyond question that our little club has, alone in all Normandy, been absolutely correct in its claim that apple brandy was actually invented in the heart of the Cotentin. The purpose of the meeting today, our chairman tells me, is to draft a letter and petition to the government, demanding that this grievous wrong be righted. Apart from a full public apology and a change of name on the label of every bottle of apple brandy produced in Normandy in perpetuity, we shall also be demanding substantial compensation for the injustice to generations of Cotentinese.

Cricket - a game which the English, not being a spiritual people, have invented to give themselves some conception of eternity.

Baron Mancroft, Conservative politician, from *Bees in Some Bonnets* (1979)

SEVENTEEN

Once again, my wife has confounded nature.

After putting the finishing touches to the cricket pitch in the top field this evening, I walked down to put the chickens away, and found the sleeping arrangements had changed again. As it was after dusk, the birds had retired for the night, and when I looked in to the coop, Barney and Gert were sitting contentedly together by one of the laying trays. In the shed by the grotto, I found Fred and Daisy canoodling on the top roosting pole. I do not share my wife's views that animals can or should obey human mores, and if someone had told me the story, I would not have believed it. But I saw what I saw. Turning the lights off and quietly closing the door, I went to the mill cottage to tell my wife that she has had her way, and her chickens are now in formal and respectable full-time relationships.

It has been a long and difficult day, and the first and certainly last cricket match to be held at La Puce has taken place. It was, even when compared to other events I have staged, a complete disaster.

Things began to go badly wrong when Bob The Builder rang to say he had forgotten to bring the cricketing equipment from England. When I called Didier in desperation, he said he had a very rare (and thus very expensive) complete set of kit which had been used and signed by the national French XI. Although I knew that France has no national cricket team, I agreed to the horrendous price so that the game could take place and put our guests in a good frame of mind for the wine tasting. Ten minutes later, our local dealer came zooming down the track in his flashy pick-up truck to deliver what was obviously nothing more than a childrens' beach set of tiny bats and wickets. When I pointed out how ridiculously small they were for grown men to use, he said that the French national team were all Basques, and were therefore very short.

Eventually, my motley crew of settlers assembled in the top field, and most looked more as if they were attending a fancy dress party than a serious cricket match. Nigel Teacher-Bell and the new lord of our manor turned up in immaculate sets of whites, but the others had obviously made little or no effort to look like proper cricketers. Despite his promises, Cameron was sporting his court robes and wig, and could hardly stand up when he struggled across the field on his rollerblades, waving a half-empty bottle of wine. Bob The Builder's concession to my strict instructions that whites were to be worn was a pair of plaster-covered overalls, and the breeder of mutant chickens was wearing his morris dancing outfit, complete with rows of small bells strapped around his calves, and a ludicrous hat with a balloon dangling from the brim.

Our opponents had also taken little notice of my request to dress properly for the event, and most were wearing their usual day-by-day combination of bib and brace overalls and brown rubber boots. The only one who had made an effort was Jean-Claude Goulot, who, his team-mates said, had stopped the traffic in St Sauveur by being seen in public without his overalls on.

Apart from both sides finally assembling an hour after the match was scheduled to start, play then had to be delayed while we rounded up a small herd of Charolais steers which wandered in from the next field and left the playing area covered in dozens of fresh and very liquid cowpats. The clearing-up operation was followed by another delay as I had to explain the basic rules of the game, and our club philosopher Jacques Délabré insisted on querying the logic of the name and location of every fielding position from silly mid-wicket to cover point.

When the match finally got under way, it was obvious that the JBC eleven had no intention of observing the rules or playing to the spirit of the game. I had to concede the toss after a fierce debate on which side of a ten franc piece would be called tails, and our supposedly impartial umpire Patrick the Post found in favour of what he called the home side. When they put us in to bat and took to the field, I counted fourteen fielders quite apart from their two bowlers, but their captain Young Pierrot said that some of his team were so elderly they needed runners, and our umpire agreed immediately.

As I took stance for the first ball, I realised that the opposing side had also cheated by inviting non-club members to play. Their opening bowler was the All-Normandy Ricard League Open Boules champion, and it was only after I stopped the match that he agreed to use Didier's rubber ball rather than his favourite stainless steel *pétanque* bombing ball. When I protested that the man was from Upper Normandy and not even a member of the Jolly Boys Club, Young Pierrot said they had held a special meeting and made him a temporary overseas member for the duration of the game. Besides, they were a man short as Old Pierrot was still indisposed.

Although I knew the side would need me to play a captain's game, I was given out leg before wicket on the last ball of the first over. When I protested that the ball had struck the bat, and pointed out that I had actually scored a boundary by reaching the hedgerow alongside the dry stream, our umpire agreed with the bowler that both my legs had clearly been in front of the wicket when I struck the ball, so I had no choice but to obey the rules, accept his decision and walk.

Eventually, our side was out for twenty-seven, all bar one of the runs being scored by Nigel Teacher-Bell. After only one over at bat, the JBC were declared the winning side when Miguel the flat-faced Portuguese plasterer hoiked one of my off-spinners over the hedge and on to a trailer of cattle maize being towed by a passing tractor. Young Pierrot said that he knew the driver and that his farm was over three kilometres away, so claimed the single stroke was worth at least a dozen boundaries, and our umpire agreed, pulled stumps and said it was high time we tried out the new Mill of the Flea wine.

If the cricket match was a disaster, the launch and tasting of our elderflower wine was a farce. I now believe that Old Pierrot has not been ill, but simply avoiding me as he knew just how bad his recipe was.

After making a short speech about my plans for marketing the Champagne of the Mill of the Flea as the first wine ever produced in Normandy, I uncorked a bottle with a flourish, and sprayed it round in the manner of a sportsman celebrating a victory. Immediately, the room was filled with a dreadful odour which, if anything, was worse than the smell from the bathtub before bottling. As the guests recoiled, a lone hornet which had made its home in the beam above the fireplace dropped like a stone to the floor. Trying to put on a brave face, I steeled myself, took a gulp and found that our new wine tasted, if anything, worse than it smelled.

Explaining that, although having a very good palate, it was obviously not quite ready to drink, I suggested the party adjourn to the terrace, and asked my wife to make a rapid trip to the Super U at St Sauveur for some real wine.

Even when I had given everyone a glass and invited them to help themselves from the buffet, the party hardly went with a swing. The French team spent most of their time looking at the food like a bomb disposal squad inspecting a rusty mine of unknown design, while the Neville-Smith-Joneses remained huddled in a corner of the yard, talking in anxious whispers while looking through the window of the mill cottage with almost as much trepidation as the JBC had been regarding the buffet table. When I asked if anything was wrong, Cynthia Neville-Smith-Jones forced a smile and asked if it were true that the same craftsmen who they had employed to restore their manor house had worked on our property. When I said that I and my wife had done most of the work ourselves, she looked happier, but said they had to get back to the manor to change their clothes, which had been caught in the spray of my new wine.

Although clearly enjoying himself dissecting the dead hornet, the entomologist had to leave early when his wife wandered upstairs and saw the multi-coloured bedspread my wife had made from odd pieces of curtain material. Before René Ribet had even got into the mood for his Whirling Dervish performance, my launch party petered out shortly after Cameron broke down, told everyone how unhappy he was, and said he was going to end it all. When one of the JBC members suggested the quickest way would be to drink one of my bottles of English wine straight down, he let out a howl of anguish, rushed up the stairs and tried to throw himself from the bedroom window. Luckily, he was so drunk he missed, and went to sleep in the roll-top bath.

As our guests drifted off, Didier took me to one side and

said that he was prepared to take all hundred bottles of my ruined wine off our hands for a token price. When I asked what he intended doing with it, he shrugged and said he would probably pour the wine down the drain, and recycle the bottles. As we helped him load his pick-up truck, he observed that my big mistake had been trying to make wine out of flowers. As the French generally believe that the worse a medicinal potion smells, the more effective it must be, it would perhaps have been a better idea to market it as a patent cure-all or horse liniment, and failing that, a very strong and effective general household cleaner.

There have been more problems with our dysfunctional duck family. As a result, I have had to create yet another refuge.

Not satisfied with the constant assaults on their own female, the Campbell gang have been making our muscovy duck's life a misery by leaping on her constantly, and Blanche had taken to spending her nights cowering under the caravan, where there is not enough head room for even those dedicated rapists to go about their brutal business. During the day, she had been wandering further away from the big pond, and yesterday did not return at dusk.

Fearing a repeat of the Big Albie episode, I told my wife I was taking Milly for a walk, and set out with a torch for a search of the fields surrounding La Puce. After several hours of blundering into barbed wire fences and bramble patches, I found her hiding in an old pig sty in the elevated field that runs the length of Hunters Walk. After I had explained what her future would be if the owner or Mr Trefle found her there in the morning, she allowed me to pick her up, and, unable to hold the torch, I had an eventful journey back to our own land.

When we arrived back at the big pond and although it

was a moonless night, the Campbells got her scent, and came thrashing across from the island. Blanche started to struggle and squawk in distress when I tried to put her down, and I could not find it in my heart to deliver her to her tormentors. As my farmer friends say that geese, ducks and chickens will all share the same quarters quite happily, I decided to put her in with Fred and Daisy for the night, but found that our normally placid hen objected to sharing her partner with another female.

When I opened the door and put Blanche in, the two birds eyed each other warily for a moment, then Daisy lowered her head, spread her wings, and charged full-tilt at what she obviously saw as a rival.

After getting the same reaction from Gert in the hen house, I took Blanche back up the path and put her in the caravan after spreading some bin liners on the floor. I shall get up early tomorrow, let her out and clean the mess up. Donella will probably be delighted to have acquired another shelter for one of her flock, but even she must agree that turning a touring caravan into permanent overnight accommodation for a large and very nervous duck is not a good idea.

She is also unaware that I have put an advertisement on our website for readers to enjoy the La Puce Experience by visiting us for dinner, then sleeping in the luxury caravan by the Big Pond so that they may enjoy nature really close to hand.

I am very worried about Blanche.

Since I frustrated the male Campbells' lust by putting her in the caravan overnight, it is as if they are taking their revenge by intensifying the attacks on her. At least a dozen times a day, the three male ducks will chase and trap her, then take it in turns to mount her. Their assaults are also becoming increasingly vicious, as if part of the fun of the game is to hurt and debase her. I am trying hard not to put a human interpretation on what is happening, but Blanche is clearly becoming more and more distressed. Her normally smoothly plump and snow-white plumage is now badly soiled and dishevelled, with a bald patch on the back of her neck where her attackers force her head under the water during the onslaughts. Though we shout and throw stones at the males when they start their attacks, they make sure to trap her in a place where we cannot get at them, and it is agonising to watch her suffer and not be able to do anything about it. We have set Milly on the males when they trap Blanche, but they just regroup and start again immediately afterwards. Although we have no illusions about the harshness of nature, what is going on seems, if anything, unnatural. If it continues, the Campbells will surely kill Blanche, which can serve them no purpose.

After helplessly watching the latest attack, we have decided something must be done. Donella refuses to even consider having the male Campbells culled, and we cannot be sure that bringing in more females will take the pressure off Blanche. For some reason, the attackers are ignoring Hen, and they seem to prefer making Blanche's life a misery. My wife has been phoning friends to see if she can find a good home for Rab, Jimmy and Gladstone, but in the meantime, we must make a safe home for our battered, sad and obviously traumatised muscovy duck.

Our latest refuge is now ready, but Blanche has disappeared again.

When I went to the big pond this morning, the Campbells were clacking angrily around the caravan, and Ermintrude had returned to her original home in the grotto. She is obviously missing her friend, and spent the day sitting miserably alone by the cascade.

After a mostly sleepless night, I got up at dawn and went in search of our missing duck. When I had spent several hours of combing the fields and surrounding woodland, I spotted a flash of white in a bramble bush deep in the wasteland opposite the mill cottage, and went in after her. After tearing my hands and face badly and twice falling in the stream, I made my capture, and struggled back to put her in the woodshed in the ruined end of the mill. Walking back from the feed store with an armful of straw bedding, I heard a frantic squawking, then saw Blanche flapping frantically towards the wasteland, with the male ducks in lustful pursuit. At the woodshed, I found the door open, although I was sure I had shot the bolt. I could not bring myself to tell Donella I had lost Blanche again, so spent another restless night, thinking of the poor creature, terrified and alone. If I do not find her tomorrow, I am going to kill the male Campbells.

Blanche is found, and safe and happy. Sitting in the mill cottage after a morning's fruitless searching, I saw her break cover from the wasteland and stumble up the track, with Gladstone and the other males charging triumphantly after her. By the time I got to the top of the track, she was stranded in the middle of the road, with cars flashing by while her pursuers chattered vindictively from the verge. After half an hour of avoiding the traffic while Milly harassed Gladstone and the Campbells, I finally cornered her in the ditch outside the farmhouse, and ran back down the track with the males flapping behind.

As dusk fell, I visited Blanche's new home. The greenhouse has a sliding door, and even the rapist ducks will not be able to force an entry. Best of all, when I arrived to say goodnight, I found the Campbells ringing her new quarters, squawking angrily as they repeatedly charged the glass in a madness of frustration at not being able to get at the victim

247

they could so clearly see.

My wife may have lost her favourite retreat for the moment, but will think that a small price to pay to make Blanche safe.

The saddest of news today. A week after our disastrous cricket match and wine launch, I summoned up the courage to face my friends at a Jolly Boys Club meeting. Immediately I walked into the bar, I could tell something was wrong, and when I saw the beret on Old Pierrot's favourite seat, I knew that our oldest member had at last had to confront and accept his mortality.

After she told me he had passed away peacefully during the night, Madame Ghislaine said she had visited Old Pierrot every day for the past month, but had promised him she would not tell his fellow members how ill he was. He did not want them to worry about him, she said, nor did he want them to realise that he, like ordinary men, could not live for ever.

She said that only a handful of the older members of the commune knew exactly when or where Pierrot had been born, and nobody knew of any relatives. For as long as anyone could remember, he had lived alone in his tumbledown cottage in the marshlands beyond Néhou, and some of the older residents thought he had arrived there shortly after completing his war service. Nobody, of course, really believed his tall stories about his adventures across the centuries, but it did no harm to indulge an old man's eccentricities. Beyond his wild tales and sometimes irascible manner, he was a good and thoughtful man, and always ready to help other members of the commune when he could. He was self-educated, and his little cottage was filled almost to the rafters with books, from which he obviously got his wide knowledge of history and nature. When she had seen him yesterday, he had told her that he did not think he would be seeing his friends again, and had given her a small gift for each of the members of our club. Passing a small oilskin book across the bar, she said it was a collection of Pierrot's favourite poems, and his thoughts on Nature and life. He told her he always meant to ask me, as a fellow writer, if I thought it worth sending to a publisher, but had not wanted me to think him vain, or that he thought anyone would be interested in the ramblings of an uneducated *paysan*.

Perhaps, he had said, I would like to keep the book, and look at it sometimes. Although I was a foreigner and from a big city, over the years he had come to realise that, in spite of my upbringing and nationality, I had the heart of a countryman.

Old Pierrot's funeral took place earlier today. It was a simple ceremony, but virtually the whole commune was at the church. When we filed past the coffin, I saw that the date of birth had been left off the plate on the lid. After the burial, I asked Jacques Délabré about it, and he said that the funeral director had wanted to inscribe an approximate date for the sake of propriety, but the members of the JBC had insisted it be left blank. They said that, although he had eventually proved that he was not immortal, it did not mean his stories of living longer than anyone else on earth were necessarily untrue. The secret of Pierrot's real age should remain unknown for all eternity.

After a subdued hour in the Bar Ghislaine, we walked home along the ancient footpath across the fields which gave the workers at the Mill of the Flea a short-cut to the church and hopeful salvation, and I said to my wife that I had been to enough funerals to last me a lifetime, and that I hoped the next I had to attend would be my own. She told me not to say such stupid things, but that she understood how I felt.

It is just over a year since my elder brother died, almost

exactly a month after my father's funeral. John told me that he had cancer on the day I heard from the surgeon about our father's shadow on the lung. My brother said he had kept the secret from us because he did not want to add to our worries, but thought I should know and be ready for whatever happened. On the day before he died, I went to his house, and by his chair, I saw a photograph of us at a scout and cub summer camp. He was only four years older than me, but in the way it ever is between brothers and sisters, it seemed sometimes that we were a generation apart. Like all brothers, we occasionally fought, and he would often complain about having to look after me and take me everywhere with him, but he was fiercely protective when I got into trouble. After our mother died, we saw each other every day, and I think we were closer during that time than ever before.

When John had given me the photograph and said he would like me to remember him as he was then, he insisted on walking with us to the car to say goodbye. While my wife drove slowly away, I looked out of the back window of the car and watched as he turned and shuffled back into the house, and somehow I knew that I would never see him again.

The struggle towards the heights is enough to fill a human heart. One must imagine that Sisyphus is happy.

Albert Camus, French novelist and essayist, 1913-60 (*Le Mythe de Sisyphus*, 1942).

EIGHTEEN

Yet again, I have contrived to be at the railway station when my ship has come in.

At Bricquebec market this morning, I came across a stall doing very brisk business in what the advertising board claimed to be a miracle insect repellent lotion. The young woman in charge told me it was a completely natural product that had been prepared from a long-lost formula, and was guaranteed to kill or at least frighten off every known variety of crawling or flying bug. She said that dozens of customers had come back and said how effective it was, and one farmer had returned to buy six more bottles to protect his cattle from warble fly after testing the preparation on his wife. As a final sales pitch, the woman said the lotion had the most dreadful smell, which proved how effective it must be. After her brief respite, Donella is back under attack from the armies of midges and other biting bugs at La Puce, so I bought a bottle in spite of the outrageous price.

When I arrived back at the mill cottage and opened the

bottle, the room was immediately filled with a rank and very familiar odour. My *Vin de la Puce* may have been undrinkable, but it has found a ready market in another guise, and I know who is cashing in on my misfortune.

I found Didier busily at work in what he calls his warehouse facility and European headquarters, but which is really an old barn behind the church at Néhou. As I walked in, he was carefully pouring my elderflower wine into the same sort of tiny bottles as I had bought at market. Dozens of my empty champagne bottles had been dumped in a plastic dustbin by the door, and the reek was overpowering.

Caught in the act, Didier confessed that he was the owner of the new stall at Bricquebec, then claimed he intended telling me about his scheme and giving me a cut of the proceeds, but had been too busy meeting the demand for the lotion. After ensuring that I still had Old Pierrot's recipe and brewing instructions, he said he has known for some time that what I had been making at La Puce was not wine. He found out when he heard that Pierrot was ill, and had followed Madame Ghislaine to his home, then gone in to pay his respects. In all honesty, he said, he liked Old Pierrot as they were both loners with a secret past. As a dealer, he also thought that the old man might have some interesting possessions he would like to sell before it was too late.

During the visit, Pierrot had asked Didier to take a message to me, explaining and apologising for a stupid mistake he had made. He had not given me the recipe and ingredients for elderflower wine, but for a natural insect repellent based on elderflowers. It was ironic, the old man had added, that modern scientists were only now discovering that the old remedies were invariably the best.

When Didier had seen the effect on the hornet at our

launch party, he had also seen the opportunity to profit from the mix-up, and, rather than tell me the truth, could not resist offering to take what I thought was undrinkable wine off my hands. Now, the truth was out, he would make amends by paying me a sensible price for the first batch, then we could share the profits from future brewings. He had already sold almost all his stock, and that without really trying. If we were to step up production and market the repellent properly, we could both end up seriously rich.

It was almost a shame to have to tell him that, although I still had the recipe for the lotion, the details on the lottery ticket did not include the secret ingredients, which were the roots and herbs that Old Pierrot had given me on the night of the party. Our old friend had probably been the only man alive to know what the vital additives were, and where to find them, and he had taken that secret with him to the grave.

15th November:

Our Indian summer is finally over and we are making ready for winter. This morning, there was a noticeable chill to the air as I walked through the water meadow to watch the mist rise from the surface of the big pond, and it was sad to think that this year, Old Pierrot will not be making his traditional prediction of the worst winter since the Great Freeze of 1642.

I am sitting by the Hobbit tree and thinking about all that has happened since our return to La Puce, and in England before we came home. Donella is not with me because the midges are at their most active at this time of day, and she has used the last of the elderflower insect repellent.

The year is dying, but will be reborn soon, and as I think

about Nature's endless and somehow reassuring cycle, Ermintrude waddles up and nudges me gently in the thigh. I am not sentimental enough to think she is being affectionate, and know that she is reminding me her breakfast has yet to be served.

Beneath one of the giant gunnera bushes lining the far side of the pond, Gert and Daisy and their partners are scratching contentedly at the rich earth. Milly is at my feet, and when I last saw her, Cato was looking thoughtfully at the surviving goldfish in the grotto. It would be interesting to know what would happen if she took on our giant eel, and for once, I don't think our werecat would come off best.

From a nearby field, I hear the sound of belligerent chattering as the Campbell gang search for Blanche, unaware that she has finally escaped them. Last Sunday morning, we came back from a shopping trip to find a strange silence at the grotto, and the chickens and ducks standing stock-still, looking across at the elevated field alongside Hunters Walk. Then we heard the blunt crack of a shotgun. By the time I had climbed the slope, the hunter was holding our poor doomed Blanche up by her feet, and making a joke with his friend. I threw him and his gun into the grotto, but unfortunately he could swim, and our giant eel did not live up to the reputation I had given it. Blanche was only a duck, but she was part of our extended family, and I had had enough of death and loss.

Although Blanche is now beyond their reach, my wife has agreed that the male ducks must go so that Hen will not suffer from their attentions. I have told her that I have been in contact with a British settler who is very fond of ducks, and that I will take Gladstone, Jimmy and Rab to their new home on the west coast tomorrow. What I have not told my wife is that the Englishman likes ducks when they are accompanied by orange sauce. My final revenge will be, quite literally, sweet.

Away from La Puce, the end of the long summer has signalled the departure of the tourists, most of the English house-hunters, and some would-be residents. After further consultation with their *feng-shui* expert, the Neville-Smith-Joneses have decided that, no matter how much they spend on the *manoir*, it will never make a happy home for them. They have put *La Grange* on the market, and gone back to Surrey. Curiously, I was somehow sad to see them go, but not as sorry as the army of local craftsmen who had hoped to get at least a winter's worth of good living out of the great house. Yesterday, I saw Mr Sourcil showing a British couple round the big house, so perhaps it will not be long before our specialists will be putting all the doors and windows back where they used to be.

We have also said goodbye to several members of our British settlers' club. Some have moved on to other parts of France through choice or necessity; some have returned across the Channel, happier or sadder, richer or poorer and perhaps wiser than before they arrived.

Before he left, Cameron called to thank us for our friendship during the summer, and for putting up with him in his blackest moments. He said he had thought that he could be a great writer and lead a different and intellectually stimulating life in another country and with other people. But, over the long summer, he came to understand that he is not really cut out for a life of artistic fulfilment and poverty, and that his heart really lies with his wife and children in Aberdeenshire, and not in the Cotentin. The best news is that she has said she will have him back.

As a reminder of their first guest at the New Algonquin, Cameron has given his rollerblades and wig to Coco and Chantal, and they now hang alongside the paper lanterns in the bar of the Flaming Curtains.

Although we still mourn the passing of Old Pierrot, things are getting back to what passes for normal at the Jolly Boys Club. Jacques Délabré has been appointed as our new life president, and Young Pierrot is now our most aged member. As a remark of respect to our late president, he will, however, remain Young Pierrot for the rest of his time with us. Our new mayor has been elected, and now that he is in office he has agreed to abandon all his electioneering promises and plans and leave things exactly as they are, which is the way we like them. The only notable scandal of late is that a rank outsider has won the regional finals of the moustache-growing championships of all Normandy. Even more shocking, the clear winner was the Widow of Négreville, who will now represent us in the finals in Rouen next month. Our only hope of avoiding disgrace, as René Ribet says, is that she will be mistaken by the judges and audience as a man, and there is a good chance of that if she can be persuaded to wear her normal going-out clothes of overalls, boots and flat cap.

Although I have made little progress on the new book, now that the summer and season of fetes and forgetfulness is behind us, perhaps I will find time during the long winter ahead to finish it in time for publication in the new year. If not, fate will take its course, and perhaps there will be no more books about our small adventures at and around the Mill of the Flea. When Schubert was working on what he hoped would be his greatest work, a friend called in and persuaded him to go to a party. The composer put his manuscript in a drawer, and it stayed there until after his death, when someone found what we know as the Unfinished Symphony. Although I do not place myself in quite the same creative league as Schubert, perhaps I should put my few pages away and hope that, after I have gone, they will be found and people will say that, had I finished it, it would have been quite a good read.

Whatever happens with my literary ambitions, the best news of the year is that we will not have to sell La Puce.

Thanks to the unprecedented interest in French property this year, my previous books have sold in their many thousands during the summer, and Mr Dette our bank manager is, if not happy with us, at least content for the moment. An unexpected bonus came last week, when the numbers Old Pierrot passed on from his friend Nostradamus finally came up. I had been using them to play the new television lottery game which takes place every five minutes in all the betting shops in France, and sat in disbelief as the winning numbers flashed up on the screen. Unfortunately, they were also picked by almost a hundred other players around the country, so my windfall will do no more than pay for a new second-hand cement mixer for Donella's next birthday present.

So we are still here in the home of our heart, and regardless of the failure of all my money-making schemes, we shall see at least another year at the Mill of the Flea. Despite the small setbacks and occasional times of sadness, my wife and I have been at our happiest at La Puce, and must make the most of every day we have left together.

As my father said and as I hope I have learned at last, tomorrow does come too soon, and it really is always later than you think.

Username PETERFFY
Password T95424